THURSDAY'S CHILD HAS FAR TO GO

KATHLEEN LUKENS *and* CAROL PANTER

> *Monday's child is fair of face,*
> *Tuesday's child is full of grace,*
> *Wednesday's child is full of woe,*
> *Thursday's child has far to go,*
> *Friday's child is loving and giving,*
> *Saturday's child has to work for its*
> *   living,*
> *But a child that's born on the Sabbath*
> *   day*
> *Is fair and wise and good and gay.*

PRENTICE-HALL, INC., ENGLEWOOD CLIFFS, NEW JERSEY

To
JACK
and
GIDEON

$\mathcal{C}$ontents

INTRODUCTION

Handicapped children are, by definition, not normal. They dwell in a different psychological world from the nonhandicapped. In fact, they live in overlapping worlds—their own and that of the normal. Together, these two worlds make up most of what they call reality. For the handicapped, even the normal world is not the same as it is for normal people; it changes more, oppresses more, frightens more. It values the handicapped less.

The two major stories that follow, "Song of David" and "The Chirping of a Sparrow," are true but fictionalized accounts of what the different worlds of two handicapped children are like. One child, young, speechless, losing contact with reality, is far from normal. The other child, older, diabetic, needing suddenly to adjust to being handicapped, is close to normal. The familiar goal of normalcy does not make real or rich the lives of these isolated children. Acceptance matters. Support counts. But what is critical to each child is his power to find value and meaning in his different world.

Doctors and psychologists are fond of telling parents "Make his life as normal as possible." But normalcy is only one standard, and surely not man's highest. To be as human as possible is, perhaps, a better standard. For to be human in the deepest sense is to be in touch with one's own existence, to know one's own feelings and thoughts, to quicken to one's inner and outer world; it is to have identity and inwardness and value that comes from oneself.

"Song of David" is about a struggle to be human. Brain-damaged before he has a chance to become a person and unable to communicate with those on whom he depends, David retreats from the world he can barely touch. His parents, faced with a speechless child who now turns away from the warmth he once enjoyed, strive to discover who he is, in what kind of world he lives, how might their worlds overlap.

When David's parents learn something of their son's inner reality, they discover how powerless he feels to make a mark on the world of men. They understand why he refuses to live in a reality that holds no appeal for him. But they also learn that reality is the atmosphere of men—without it even his inner life is gasping—and that their son must take in reality even as all men must breathe.

✳

More often than not, however, it is not the child's disability that prevents him from sensing the fullness of his being, but his social and psychological handicap. Experts have argued, for example, that the perceptual world of the blind and deaf could mean as much and be as "good" as that of the normal, if the sighted and the hearing did not make blindness and deafness handicaps.

The loss of confidence in her bodily functioning which Jane, the diabetic child, experiences in "The Chirping of a Sparrow" is a disability. It limits Jane's mobility and comfort and makes her inadequate to the demands of certain normal situations. She is tired, or thirsty, or hungry, or weak when normal children are not. But Jane's disability need not have been a handicap. The child's adjustment to her chronic illness might have occurred rather painlessly had the child been able to see her unpredictable weakness as only one of her many characteristics and not her most important one.

"The Chirping of a Sparrow" is the authentic story of a child required to be normal, who was not. It concerns the apparent need of the normal world to make the loss of an important tool and the loss of certain functions, a loss of value. It points up the tendency of parents to see abnormality as inferiority. It demonstrates the process by which a disability becomes a handicap, the one thing that stands in the way of parental approval and, therefore, self-approval.

Finally, "The Chirping of a Sparrow," which might have been written about almost any physical disability, illustrates the psychological hazards of a hopeless but prevalent search for the unattainable goal of normalcy, just as the essay at the end of the book, "The Handicapped Society," sheds light on the social values that lead parents into the search that so often ends in maladjustment.

✳

Withdrawal from the world of normal people, on the other hand, can be as unrealistic as the need to "pass" for normal. The life space of the physically and mentally sound is larger and open to greater possibilities than the life space of one afflicted with any specific handicap. The normal world will always be a part of the handicapped child's reality, a reality he can't, with impunity, deny. "The Very Image of a Child" is the story of a loving mother's overprotective response to society's power to reject her mongoloid daughter. Perhaps it will remind the reader, especially if he is a parent of a handicapped child, that despite the prohibitions, there exist in society people who value those who need most to be valued. It should be a reminder also that through contact with others, the handicapped child can learn the social skills and self-love he needs to be accepted as a person.

❊

What kind of life pattern an individual child ought to have, will not, of course, be resolved by this book. One of the aims of the authors is to raise questions about pat solutions to the challenge of handicap. Any decision carries with it guilt. For even the choice to care for an abnormal child may be decided at some expense to the healthy. "For the Best" is the story of two young parents of a severely orthopedically handicapped son, who discover that *not* making a decision is also a choice. For them, the beginning of wisdom is to set their own course, however uncertain it may be.

❊

Any story of a handicapped child living at home is also the story of a handicapped family, for the family not only cares for the child, but takes on the stigma of his social handicap. From the family, the child derives his standards, his values and his self-image. But from society, the family derives *its* standards, *its* values and *its* social image. The reader may find in the pages that follow that his concern is not just with how handicapped is the child, but indeed, how handicapped is the family?

All the stories that compose this book happened or are happening to real members of handicapped families. We chose fiction rather than case studies to dramatize the life situations of the handicapped and their families because we believe that while objective fact can give knowledge, it is the revelation of inner life that truly gives understanding.

Kathleen Lukens and Carol Panter

*

SONG OF DAVID
By Kathleen Lukens

*

CHAPTER ONE

David spit on the window pane and watched the spittle roll slowly down the glass. Beyond the window, the sun shone on men piling bricks to build a house. Trowels flashed but David didn't see them. Hammers rang but David didn't hear them. He took a pencil and lapped it rhythmically back and forth in the spittle. It was as if a windshield wiper were stroking away the rain.

The scrape of the pencil came ever so slightly, ticking, nearly purring. And the purr had a curiously muffling effect. It beat back the intense blue sky, blunted the stabbing red rose in the garden. The world sank back in a bluish blur.

So often in the midst of David's game, his mother protested: "Look at the house, David, the bricks are getting higher." Or "See the sky," or something equally simple and direct. But David did not look up. He tried not to hear her. He was learning to avoid the terrible pull of sights and voices, his peculiar lust to touch and break what he liked the most.

The fierce green of the grass, the silver lids of the salt and pepper shakers, the white mealy contents of the soap box did not merely attract him. They seized him, the way magnets seize particles of steel. Some sense, some feel, there must be some spirit in things. Something David could seize. How often he had taken the little bell of his pull toy and struck it, and struck it, and struck it, until the bell's core flew out across the room clinking dully into silence. Done! He would not hear it again or, rather, half-hear it. For so differently was David constructed from other children, nearly everything he saw, felt, heard, lay only on the tip of his under-standing. Nothing matched. Nothing exactly echoed expectation. If only he could be sure that there was one thing he saw exactly the way other people saw it. But something was always missing. An important thing. If he could not find it, he would destroy that which reminded him of its loss.

2

Lately, David tried hard to avoid these fits of destruction. His head hurt from banging it and his hand from biting it. Harsh world where nothing worked! He would hide from it. Play windshield-wiper. Perhaps through the rhythm of this soundless music restore his soul.

David's parents, Mr. and Mrs. Fitzgerald, had begun to worry about his "blank look," as his grandmother called it. It became noticeable around the time of David's third birthday last month. "No," his father remembered, "he was doing that thing with the pencil back around five months ago, about the time the baby was born."

"My beauty boy," Mrs. Fitzgerald called him. A friend had said he ought to be a model. Wouldn't she know, she's an artist? David had regular, almost perfect features, but his eyes, they were special. Gray-blue, bright as raindrops. Alert, discerning eyes. Her father used to call them "lamps."

You couldn't deny David looked bright. His mother imagined him to be the brightest of her four sons. Not that he had given her any signs. It was mostly his responsiveness. And his eyes. They seemed deep at times, and desperate with experience. But, did they see things the way she saw them?

David was a late talker. More a nontalker, his father corrected his reflections. "He's three now and I bet he can't say ten words. Then again, children have different developmental time clocks." But when does their experience begin to merge with ours?

David worked at words. No child ever worked harder. He would screw up his face the way a runner tightens up his body at the starting line. Then off! Some sound ought to come uncoiling from his brain. But no sound came. Rather, no word came. Just screams, chuckles, shouts, whimpers, animal noise.

David had been different from the other children almost from the time he had been born, but Catherine Fitzgerald, and, for that matter, Jim too, could tolerate a wide range of difference without viewing with alarm. As a toddler, David had never been tempted by stray pins, open pill bottles, or coffee grounds the way the other Fitzgerald babies had been. His mother had to teach him to eat a cookie when he was eight months old. David never explored with his mouth.

"He always had such a terrible fear of falling," Catherine reminded Jim that night as they washed and dried the dishes after supper. "Remember how scared he was when my mother carried him downstairs? Frantic." I always thought she was too rough, Catherine said to herself. And she pictured her mother bouncing downstairs with David tense and trembling in the crook of her large arms.

"He used to get so scared he'd bite her," Jim agreed.

It was 7:30. Homework time for the three eldest. They worked in the parlor. David had stuffed three cookies into his mouth the way a pelican stores fish in his beak. He sat ruminating on the kitchen floor.

"He's been pretty cautious about the stairs ever since," Jim polished a dish. "Too cautious for a three-year-old kid. Half the time he won't even come downstairs unless one of us carries him."

"But he goes down the five porch steps all by himself."

"I know. Maybe it's the baby. Maybe," Jim said, drawing on his schoolteacher background, "he's regressing on account of the baby."

Or maybe he's slow, Catherine wanted to add. But she restrained herself from voicing her greatest fear. Catherine Fitzgerald was a bright, educated woman, mother of five, who still had time for painting and The League of Women Voters. What would she do with a slow child?

"I got a letter from my mother this morning," Catherine tried to change the subject. It had contained an encouraging clipping on late talkers from the New Orleans *Time-Picayune*. Maybe it's like Aunt Lilly says, David is just spoilt. She remembered the joke about the four-year-old that her friend had made a point of telling. The child, never having spoken a syllable in his life, suddenly burst into speech. "Why haven't you talked up before?" his joyful parents supposedly asked. "I didn't have to," went the punch line, "things ran so smoothly up till now."

The cookies consumed, David struggled to his feet, pushed open the kitchen door and disappeared into the parlor.

He's all right, Catherine said to herself, anybody can see that child's all right.

A minute passed. Catherine first heard screams. Then a thud, young bodies wrenching on the parlor floor. Jim flew out of the kitchen.

"Dad!" Catherine Fitzgerald heard a wail rising from the parlor, "Dad, he wrote on my homework again!"

Catherine got up. She rushed towards the rhythmical bump,

bump, bump coming from the parlor table. That would be David banging his head. "Cripes," she shrieked as she caught the child's thrashing body, smoothed his hair, and felt the lumps swelling on his forehead. "God, why does he do that?" she cried.

❋

David loved the long car ride to Grandma's house the day before Thanksgiving. It was the movement he loved, the whirr of the engine, fluid shapes advancing and retreating, his private world knifing through the wind. Nothing could touch him; not form, not sound, not color. Somehow, the rhythm of the ride hushed them; the rush through space tuned them down.

On occasion, he saw. The gray-brown waves of hair on the back of his mother's head.

Or, he heard his father's voice: "I don't know what you're worried about, Cass, my mother's a tolerant soul."

Mostly, he stood, with the voices of his family rubbing cheerfully together. In silent music. In perfect peace.

They went to the aquarium on Saturday. Grandma kept the baby. They wanted to bring David out of himself. "Get him to enjoy things the way the rest of us do."

Outside, Jim spoke to David with mock reproach, "If you're going to throw a fit today, do it now. *Before* I buy the tickets."

Mark, Danny, and Jonathan raced right past the indoor exhibits on to the outside pools where a seal was catching a ball on his nose. Their parents and David lagged half a block behind.

"Better keep an eye on them," Jim speeded up.

David saw Jim moving ahead of them and tried to follow. But then as the crowd surged around his father and swallowed him up, David screamed. The pieces of world stuck so precariously together were coming unglued. David threw himself upon a wasted flower bed and banged his head.

In desperation, his mother seized the thrashing child and carried him, her knees stinging with kicks, to a bench where she held him tight to her and tried to speak softly.

❋

"He'll be back, David. Can't you see?" she moaned.

Faces turned toward them; Catherine thought they seemed irked and testy. David's head whacked backward against her ribs and her hand, bitten and bloody, was wet with David's tears. Catherine held tighter as if she would stifle David with a bear hug. She hated Jim for having gone away.

Around David, the world kept collapsing. Every sight, sound, smell, feeling impinged on him at once, amplified. It was as if he were in a tiny room with a radio, the television, a movie, sirens, and whistles all going full blast. He struggled to catch the meaning of just one of them. If only one sense could bind his attention and hold it fast.

The indoor section of the aquarium contained a huge, cylindrical fish tank two stories high with a wide, spiral ramp wound around it. In the darkened room, the lighted tank glowed with bright, green water. It illumined fish of every type and hue.

Subdued lamps lit the path along the ramp. It was those lamps that were to resettle David's world.

Having been dragged indoors where he rejoined his male family, David broke free and headed for the ramp lamps. Each light pulled him toward it as if it had the force of gravity. He ran on, up the ramp, through crowds of people, around the circle at the ramp's top, and then on down, touching each lamp as he reached it, hovering at times over the dimmed lights.

His oldest brother, Mark, pursued him. He picked David up to make him look into the fish tank. But the green light inside it was diffuse and dreamlike, the swimming shapes too obscure for David to fix upon. He saw but he did not grasp. Instead, he tore himself loose and the child, obsessed, ran down, down the spiral walkway, then up, up past the human shapes silhouetted against the murky tube of the tank; ascending, descending, until at last he fell, puffing wearily at his father's feet.

"Dad," Mark asked as he watched David, his head down, soft, light strands swirling from his scalp like rings of water. "How come he can't look at things the way we do?"

"I think he could, Mark," Jim answered. "If we could only find the right thing, I think he could."

David, rested, felt himself being lifted up. He tilted slightly, trembled, but fell against a solid chest, smelled sweet smoke, felt the splint-hard arm of his father.

A few minutes later, the Fitzgeralds had seated themselves in a huge theater whose stage was another great, greenish fish tank, this one rectangular. The boys bounced on their seats in excitement. As the crowd pressed into the surrounding chairs, David twisted on his father's lap.

They were awaiting the arrival on stage of two trained porpoises whose alleged feats in water had been cataloged several times by the children.

"This is crazy," Catherine was saying. "He's never going to sit this out."

Jim had the same fears, but it annoyed him when Catherine gave up too easily. "Dammit, we came here to see the porpoises, didn't we? The other kids have to live, too." If the lights had distracted David away from the dimly-lit cylinder tank, he reasoned, other lights might possibly draw him in. When the spotlights went on in the porpoise tank, David might be impelled to look at them. He just might get the idea. Anyway, it was worth a try.

It seemed an eternity before the spotlights went on. Applause. The announcer droned on with acknowledgments to trainers and producers, the early life history of the porpoises, scuba commercials. David was whining, rolling his head back and forward, nipping at his father's hands. Jim held one hand tight around David's wrists; the other gripped his struggling legs. At last, a porpoise swam into the great, green-yellow lit tank and began performing. Jim held up David and made him look.

"David, look at the fish," Catherine pleaded. "See the nice big fish!"

David was struggling, trying to turn and look back at his father.

Danny screamed, "David, hey, David, look at the fish."

A huge, scarlet-colored bar had slowly begun descending on wires from the ceiling of the sea theater. It was brilliant, a gash in the yellow light. It trembled over the beryl-green water.

David seemed to be turning toward it.

And then, an enormous, smiling silver fish, popping out of a hole like a torpedo tube, sailing up the lighted water, arched itself over the scarlet bar, effortlessly, like an arrow in flight.

The boys hollered. The crowd roared.

As Catherine and Jim turned toward David, he was standing on the chair pointing unmistakably to the tank containing the porpoise.

"Fish."

"He said 'fish,' " the parents screamed at each other.

"Ffffish," David chuckled his applause.

CHAPTER TWO

David touched every object in the toy lady's room. He poked them the way children poke bubbles. He reached out to them as if they were images liable to disappear. Once he had assured himself that each truck, pencil, chair had thickness and weight, David ran to his father's side. He tapped Jim's hand three times as if obeying some magic ritual, then leaned his body heavily against his father's.

"Ah, David," the lady psychologist peered over her desk. "Do you like the toys?"

David didn't answer. Jim began stroking his hair. "I already told her over the phone he doesn't talk," Jim said to himself.

"He doesn't talk," Jim said aloud.

The psychologist did not look at the father. Nor did David turn his eyes toward her. He hardly ever looked directly at anyone.

"What's this? What do you call it?" The lady sat next to David now. She pointed to a large picture of a dog and asked again, "What's this?"

David looked. Not at the pictures but at the toy lady's glasses. At first, his eyes had merely glanced at them as they sat on the blotter, little suns swimming on their lenses. But now they absorbed him. Shapes floated in them. Colors came wet. They struck the dulled water of his senses with their dazzling reflection.

"How about this one? What's this?" The middle-aged Dr. Rosen showed David another card, a red cat smiling. She had maneuvered her body in front of the glasses so that David could no longer see them.

David trembled and craned to get a glimpse of the glasses. Suddenly he spotted them, and leaping forward he felt the closing gate of his father's arm. Jim held fast to the kicking, bleating body of his child.

"It's my fault," the psychologist reassured as she placed the glasses safely in her desk. "I should have known they'd present too much distraction."

A few minutes later, David was piling blocks to build a tower. The tower completed, he went on to form archways and fences; slabs that leaned against each other the way he leaned against his father.

David did not look up. His face wore a smile as he pushed a little car along the floor. Then suddenly deciding he was thirsty, David searched for a spigot in the room. He found a chair, pushed it over to the sink, climbed up, poured himself a glass of water, drank it, returned to the blocks, and built a bridge. David beamed as he tapped the lady's hand.

"Wuah." David framed the word for "water" with his lips as he sat playing "airplane" on the floor. He tried to whisper it. He sucked breath as if he felt the thrill of danger. It was easier to drag chairs across rooms, to climb up to the cabinet, pull down a cup, and set the stream of water flowing. Much easier than to say "wuah." "Wuah" took concentration. It took an internal searching and a finding. It took a spark leaping across some gigantitude of space. It took silent meaning, unspoken sound, each looking forward to a union. It took the mesh of voice and symbol, their movement together down the lip-formed, tongue-shaped corridor. All, to make a word.

David couldn't draw a circle. He took the pencil and made close, tight strokes, up and down, up and down, bunches of thick, wild grass. The toy lady drew a circle and David filled it in. He smiled at the kindly woman and leaned against her.

He shrieked when a puzzle fell apart, when a pipe bowl came unpasted from its pipestem. Room, floor, ceiling, stay together!

David wouldn't bang two fire trucks together, not even after the psychologist showed him how. He laughed at first at her rowdy collisions. But then, when he felt the ripples of anger churning inside himself, he broke off watching her and sent the trucks rolling in two directions.

David was stringing beads. The psychologist, amiable and warm, looking arty in her dark skirt and blouse, shifted her gaze from the child to the man who brought him.

He was frowning with concern. Still, he was lean and boyish. Thirty-five he said. He looks younger.

The three beads David had managed to fit on the long, white string slid off and clattered on the floor. Jim bent slightly forward as if he would help David pick them up.

He seems approachable, Dr. Rosen thought, but to some extent detached. A certain manly, unmartyred sense of responsibility. Likeable. She smiled at Jim.

"He doesn't seem to have the fine motor control most children have developed by this age," she began her explanation when Jim turned at last in her direction. "I want to see how he is on anti-gravity play before I tell you what I have." She got up and crossed the room toward David.

It surprised David. After all, she had been talking to his father. Now the toy lady suddenly picked him up, held him by the waist, and began to whirl him round. His feet flew outward. He felt himself slip. The walls were melting, the ground giving way. David's teeth clenched against a sense of abject helplessness. His nails cut his palms. The beads of his eyes grew terrible and black. The whole order of the room as he had come to trust it suddenly lost its scheme. It whirled about him, on toward castastrophe, the death of solidity, the shapeless terror of the shapeless night. "AYyyy" pierced the air. A sound, some foreign, animal echo of a cry struggled out at last from David's lips. Trembling, he landed.

※

Catherine checked the kitchen clock. Eleven-thirty. David and Jim had been gone more than two hours. "Longer than I thought." And why? She'll never tell us what's the matter. They never do. Psychologists are vague. They talk about egos, and complexes, and rejections but they never tell you what to do. It's the mother's fault. She's always to blame. She thinks she loves her child but underneath it turns out she hates him. I wonder why Jim took him. The pediatrician said David is normal. A little slow, but normal."

A car slowed to a stop in front of the house. Catherine heard its motor die and its door slam shut. David butted the door open with his head and rushed into the kitchen with a fistful of candy. Jim was solemn.

"He's brain-damaged," Jim blurted out. "She thinks it's minimal but she doesn't know for sure."

"What?" Catherine gasped. "Brain-damaged?" She reeled as if she had been struck. Her eyes beamed bewilderment and distrust.

"I shouldn't have told you now," Jim wanted to cry. He confronted Catherine's beaten-dumb expression with a mixture of anger and remorse. Why had he always given Catherine bad news blunt as a hammer stroke? Why had he not prepared her?

"She thinks he's in very good shape, considering," Jim spoke coolly. He sank into a kitchen chair beside his wife. It was quiet in the room for the moment, the quiet in the eye of a storm. When, he wondered, would she unlease her usual pageant of emotion that would help him restrain the spectacle of his own?

"Let's face it," he tried to provoke her. "We always knew there was something wrong."

"Brain-damaged? For cripes sake what's brain-damaged?" asked Catherine. "Retarded? Mental?" Her voice climbed higher with every question.

"It's damage to the brain," Jim fumbled awkwardly. He couldn't even find some useful words.

"I'm trying to be calm, Jim," Catherine spit through gritted teeth. "What do you mean by saying David's in great shape considering? Isn't that a little like saying 'Except for two heads, the kid is fine'?"

"No, it's not like having two heads," he shot back. "You know if you'd stop screaming at me," Jim was screaming, "I'd be glad to explain it in detail. It isn't my fault our kid is damaged. It just doesn't happen to be my fault."

"Is it mine? You tell me, Jim, is it mine?"

"No, no, no, no, no, no, no. Do we have to fight about it, Catherine? Do you have to regard every problem, every pinch of the purse strings, every family crisis, every goddam ripple, as a conspiracy against your personal happiness? Do you have to blame me?"

"But I haven't blamed you," Catherine spoke the truth with bludgeoned innocence, Jim's eyes growing narrower with guilt. "I haven't (O, how righteously the injury sank in) . . . blamed you."

She quivered. Tears of self-pity geysered up from the well of her stored mistreatments, primed by some deeper, purer grief to come. Catherine wept. She saw Jim's remorse. But still she wept.

Glaring, he watched the rills of Catherine's misery flowing down the hummocks of her face. "Women, they're free to do that," Jim muttered. With Catherine you could count on it almost. "Uncivilized, ridiculous, I'm supposed to feel like a rat."

A tear hung from the cliff of Catherine's nose. He thought, she never pretends an emotion she doesn't feel.

At last, Catherine sniffled, snatched a tissue out of the debris on the kitchen workboard, and wiped her reddened, swollen eyes. Water was boiling over on the stove. Catching her husband's silent, sullen profile, she rose to stir the pot and lower the gas. "Get David." She made a stab at her own recovery. "He's playing that pencil thing at the cellar window. Please put him up for a nap while I get the lunch."

Jim didn't answer. "Now she'll listen," he told himself as he sprang to his feet, relieved. "That's Daddy's big boy," he sang to David as he carried him up to bed. "That's Daddy's great big David boy."

"Big boy, humph," Catherine heard her son's 'Da Da' with reproach. "Some big boy. The big boy that never grows up." She grinned miserably at the pen markings on her new tablecloth as she set out the silverware for lunch. "You work for a thing," she thought bitterly, "because you know it's going to grow. How can you care for someone when he stops?"

Catherine sank into a kitchen chair newly gashed, David's latest work. "Everything stops. We all die," she corrected herself, a tear sliding out of her eye. "That doesn't keep us from living. Did I expect something I had no right to expect? Do you get something back from a child? Or, do you give him your joy, your sadness, all that is alive in you, because it is painful not to give?"

"I could ask 'Why did You do this to me?' " Catherine glared at the brass Christ hanging from His crucifix on the pockmarked wall. "I see he hasn't smashed or broken You . . . But then," she was honest, "I can't think of any reason why You shouldn't . . . I didn't know how crippled he was, how alone. You can't pity what you respect. He was more special, always more beloved."

"Any kind of mother," Catherine cried suddenly. "If I were any kind of mother I would have known. Back then, before I began to look. I didn't want to know. I let him lie up there because he was quiet and I could paint and feel sorry for myself for being pregnant and let him die of loneliness. How could I know? A child is a person when he talks. Before that you only sense him. You listen for his cries, you weep his tears but you don't really know. Because he is. You love a child because he is."

When Jim came down he was mumbling to himself like an actor

trying to recall his lines. "Hyperactive, distractible, poor object relations," he rehearsed the words and definitions the psychologist had carefully explained.

They sat silently for the moment, hurting, not knowing then how many times they would sit like this, buried alive in the same crypt. Then suddenly they would be talking at once and laughing and fighting and remembering that only individual people die alone. Together, they are forced to live.

"You know, Cass," Jim put in cheerfully, "Ninety percent of David's brain works fine . . . Of course, some important parts don't."

Catherine took the dishes from the shelf.

"The working parts try to compensate for the parts that don't work, but they don't quite make it; so the whole mechanism is affected. The brain is kind of thrown off, if you know what I mean."

"Thrown off?" Catherine plugged in the electric coffeepot.

"Well, like a machine. It doesn't operate as smoothly and efficiently as a normal, undamaged brain. But as time goes by, if, and it's a big 'if,' the kid doesn't develop emotional problems because of the brain damage, he can approach a normal life."

Catherine blew her nose. "It's hard to pity her," Jim was thinking. "She has too good an opinion of herself. She has friends, loads of them. Standing in the community. Didn't they show her sketches at the library?"

Catherine filled the empty sugar bowl. "I'm listening," she said as she looked up, and finally, at Jim.

"You know how overactive he is, how he runs around touching everything and everybody he sees, how he breaks everything, how he seems to be at the mercy of every sight and sound . . ."

There was a cloud in Jim's eyes, Catherine noticed, one that did not match the quick of his voice or of his diction. Anger had been replaced by sorrow. His soul was dying in him from remorse. What had David suffered, his eyes asked? What stretch of horror for this helpless child? Still he spat the bright words past the phantom of this other being, this separate, apart, cruelly injured child of his, and the father could make no reparation.

"Will he be normal or won't he?" Catherine cried, her fright reawakened by Jim's mood.

"He could be," Jim answered dully. "Dr. Rosen doesn't know.

ks the chances are good. At least, she thinks he'll be able to
after a few years of special training, play therapy, luck. A
ends on us."

ll he be able to grow up and care for himself?"

e thinks so, Cass," Jim said. "She hopes so."

Say you'll try, he wanted to beg her. Reassure me. "It may," he
mumbled, "take heroic effort."

Catherine did not speak. It was no easy choice for her to opt for
noble self-effacement against the comforts of self-pity. She lived
with David. Heroism to her was that which occupied a stage, an
act to be exalted, something brave, quick, colorful, and clean.
Where she and David dwelled was not like this. Ah yes, there was
joy, love, little bits of courage, even determination at times. But
mostly there was gray. Not merely the monotonous, the drab, the
incessant repetition of words she hoped he'd repeat, but the ugliness. The soiled, torn, smeared, fetid ugliness that made up the
routine of daily life. There would be no medals for Catherine, no
recognition, perhaps not even signs of encouragement. Just the
endless, heartless pricking of necessity, that she endure, that she
respond.

Jim had taken the morning off from work to take David to see
Dr. Rosen. Now, considering the verdict, he decided to call the
school and tell them he wouldn't be in that afternoon either.

They lunched on leftover spaghetti and meat balls, for which
Catherine was irked with herself. The baby, Maggie, had awakened
and demanded milk just as lunch had been prepared. She had to
feed Maggie a bottle with her left hand and roll the strings of
spaghetti with her right. "Poor planning," Catherine told herself.

As they sat eating, Jim explained that David's tantrums were
not tantrums at all but a "catastrophic reaction," an implosion of
rage and despair; they could hear the rumble of their son's crib
pounding upon the floor above. David had resorted to rocking his
whole body backward and forward in his crib as long as Jim could
remember. Whenever the child lost control, began biting and
kicking or whining, they could place him in his crib and be assured
he would soothe himself with forceful, incessant rhythmic movement. David's eyes would become transfixed, and he would hurl
himself mightily against the mattress for an hour before he went to
sleep.

"Background music," Jim glanced at the ceiling and observed

"We're going to have to get ceiling tile. Look at that plaster!"

"Jim, I think he's getting worse," said Catherine.

"Just bigger," was Jim's response. "Rosen thinks David's okay. She said she never saw a kid with so much drive to learn. He knows he's different, but he tries desperately to make up for it. He knows people are trying to help him. She says he's affectionate, cooperative, ambitious, and it's all due to our handling of him. Doesn't that make you feel good?"

Catherine blushed. Maggie struggled upright, tore the bottle out of her mouth, and let it fall into Catherine's spaghetti. "I'm going to handle this one . . . with a shot in the head."

Jim tried to bring his mind sharply back to the details of Dr. Rosen's explanation. He saw that Catherine's deep-set, blue-lit oils of eyes dwelled on him with an air of speculation. "Can I handle it?" she must be wondering. He knew that she would take her cue from him.

"When a kid's brain is damaged the way David's is," Jim went on, seducing her good will with ideas, "the filtering mechanism in his brain doesn't work right. Everything impinges on him at once."

"Impinges?"

"You know, strikes him, batters him. Every sound, every sight, every feel, every smell, everything." David's father was warming to the task. "Now we're normal; our filtering mechanism is intact. That means we can listen to the radio one minute, listen to each other the next and presumably never get confused."

Jim jumped up and turned on the radio. A singing commercial lurched into life.

"For a split second," Jim shouted, "you were listening to this commercial but now that I'm talking, you're listening to me. The song has slid into the background because you've shifted your attention to what I say."

"It would slide better if you'd turn that thing down," cried Catherine.

Jim moved closer to his wife. "If the radio is on too loud," he went on, "you'll see it as a distraction from the main focus of your attention—namely me, but you'll never doubt where you intend the focus to be." Jim flicked the radio off and continued. "By the same token, we can shift our attention back and forth when we hear David rocking, Maggie whining, the man from the cleaner's at the door."

"But David can't. Right?" Catherine put in. His eyes smiled when she rejoined the conversation. They scanned hers for resolution, for will, for the fortitude of life.

"Right," he beamed as if she had said something good instead of something sad. Abstraction had seduced him as well. "His brain can't filter properly," he rushed on, "the background from the noises in the foreground. . . ."

"Which is why he's always going off the track."

"Why he's distractible. His focus is very poor, if it exists at all."

"He can't pay attention?"

"More like, his attention's drawn to everything he sees. Every sound in the room. And each one strikes with equal intensity."

Catherine supposed that was why David was never satisfied, why he had to touch everything and everybody, why every time he heard a noise he had to discover whence it came. She spoke over the thump, creak, thump of incessant rocking. "Remember the aquarium, the way he was pulled toward the lights?" she cried at Jim. "Oh, it all makes sense now. It all makes sense."

Jim laughed. Meaning. There is joy in meaning. It does not undo the damage, unmake the problem, but it gives cause. It is good to understand.

"Remember how he saw the porpoise when the house lights dimmed?" Catherine cried again. "He was able to focus on it then."

But now she fretted, "But not much lately, Jim. Lots of times he seems to have given up."

"Some kids react by withdrawing into themselves after awhile, but Rosen didn't seem to think David has. Since they can't be selective about what they sense, lots of them tune the whole world out."

"He does that. More and more he does that. Don't you know what I mean, Jim? That's that glazed look. That windshield wiper thing. Maybe that's even why he rocks."

"Could be," Jim conceded distractedly, not knowing then how right Catherine was or how deep David would sink into the abyss of his internal world before Jim would see it too. "The psychologist thinks his contact's good. Of course, he doesn't pay much attention to other kids. Golly, I wish they'd try to draw him out."

"He's especially strange toward her," Catherine referred to
Maggie, now banging the table with a spoon. "Every time I take
her up for a bottle, David goes blank. He acts as if he doesn't see
her."

Neither of them had any appetite for lunch. Maggie had
knocked Catherine's plate on the floor and had been put to bed. In
the background, David's rocking was like the movements of a
clock, striking away the seconds, the minutes. Through the window came the dazzle of sky, the sharp, crystalline azure of the
winter.

Mr. and Mrs. Fitzgerald were hungry for information, to discover the mechanics of David's special problem. They recalled
David's awkwardness, his poor judgment of size, shape, distance,
direction and relative motion, his incessant tripping and falling and
bumping into things. They discussed "perseveration," his difficulty
in shifting from one situation to another, how, after he had identified a duck correctly once, he would persist in seeing a duck on
every page of his animal book even though there were no ducks in
sight. The dimensions of their problem they did not dare face with
the brunt of unprepared emotion. They had to split it, break it into
parts they could understand. Know first, then feel, so that feeling
was bounded by the knowing.

"How'd he do on the tests?" Catherine burst into Jim's ex-
position.

"Great on the blocks. But frankly Cass, and you know it
anyway, he's retarded in almost every area."

"Yes, I know it," Catherine answered dully. Hadn't she watched
him, stared at him looking for something, she knew not what, lain
awake nights wondering what she was searching for? Hadn't she
compared him secretly with all the other three-year-olds who
came to visit, or even who passed them on the street? "You can't
live with a child and care for it and not know. Remember when
that pediatrician fellow said he was normal, and we kept saying
how relieved we were? Well, we were only relieved for an hour or
a day. He said the sun was shining but he never even bothered to
look out the window. We knew it was raining all the time."

Silent for a moment, Jim fixed his pale, white forehead into a
frown and plumbed again his recollection. "A lot of these kids," he
forced the conversation back again to the diagnosis, "a lot respond

to all these unfiltered pulls by becoming overactive or 'Hyperki-netic' is what she said. They are 'stimulus-bound,' uh, uh, impul-sive. Everything attracts them."

"Especially drawers, I'll bet." It was like fitting the pieces of a puzzle.

"Uh-huh. They open every drawer in the house, look in every pocket, take everything apart."

Catherine reenvisioned their endless, frustrating searches for missing tools, the screws out of the television set, lost light bulbs, sink plugs, lamp switches, stove knobs. "Why, remember the time he took the hinges off the door?"

"Oh boy, I remember. And you said 'How smart he is!' "

"I can't believe he's dumb. I still can't believe it," Catherine moaned.

Maybe he could change just enough so he could pass, so no one need know. The idea went racing through Jim's head. But then he heard the thump of David's rocking, and the chirrup of David's unprompted laughter, strange sounds that roused Jim in the night. "Pass for what?" he damned himself bitterly. "Pass for human?" He heard Catherine come at him again.

"If your brain is out of whack, you can't be bright."

"Well, if you could," he watched the floor quake on the ceiling, "what's intact is more efficient if you're bright."

She poured a new round of coffee, crying dumbly; her face reddened when she cried—she looked more Irish, one of the wild, red Celts raging in the forest—it set his hackles rising, his fears astir.

Catherine gulped. "But if you can't concentrate on anything for more than a second, how can you learn?" She ought not cry. She knew his fear of sentiment, his savage contemptuousness of sham. "Didn't you say he couldn't concentrate?"

"Rosen says he can't grasp the wholeness of things," Jim's fore-head came unfurrowed. "He can't integrate sounds and sights into a meaningful pattern. He can't make sense out of what he sees. Remember when he tore the bell out of the pull toy?"

"He banged it as if he didn't realize that all it's supposed to do is ring." Catherine answered, "I guess he didn't get the point."

Jim was still a moment listening to the rocking as if the sound joined him with David in communion. Words drove David off into a figment of the mind, but the rocking made him real and a person.

He pictured him, his dullness, his electric spasmodic bursts of energy, his living look of helplessness and trust. He recalled the dreams he had had for him, how he and Catherine had regarded each child as a kind of experiment, each bound to improve as they went along. Surely, the glorious mixture of their genes—strength, beauty, passion, reason, righteousness—would forge heroic types, Jim mused with cynical disdain.

"Why doesn't he talk?" Catherine asked. "I mean, Jim, if I could just get through to that kid. If he could just get through to me, I know I could help him."

So he was going to have to tell her that part, too. "I hate to give it to you all at once," came Jim's drone of resignation. "But he may also have aphasia. He may be injured in the speaking part of the brain. He'll talk but he may never have normal speech." Why must she incessantly demand answers when I have no answers, structure when I have no structure to give? "Speech is a very complicated process. The brain has to be able to receive words correctly," he explained. "It has to integrate words with ideas and transmit properly. And then there's the impulses to the mouth. They have to work."

"It can't be that hard," Catherine said peevishly. "Everybody else talks."

"Everybody else," came Jim's cool answer, "doesn't have lesions in the speech area. "Lesions," he had grown tired of it now, "lesions are hurts. Lesions anywhere along the line can cause some form of aphasia. That's loss of speech. These hurts never heal. Sometimes, especially in a kid the age of David, there are ways to get around them. They say you can even teach the brain."

It was past three and the boys returned from school, a herd of disrobing goats, climbing shelves to get cookies, dropping jackets on kitchen chairs, dripping snow, red-eared, pulling out notices demanding annual dental examinations, attendance at the P.-T.A., fifty cents for a class trip, crying, "Hi, Dad, what are you doing home?" And David stroked the spittle on the window.

After supper when the children had gone to bed, Catherine carried three enormous loads of dried clothes up from the cellar, got out the ironing board, and began to iron in the parlor. There was a play on television. Jim half-watched it while he marked papers for his class. Upstairs, two of the boys talked in the dark. David was rocking.

"Sit down, will ya?" Jim called to Catherine. "Didn't you know tonight's the maid's night off?"

"Who's going to do the boys' school shirts?" Catherine answered gaily. "Maybe you know a couple of unemployed fairies."

"I could let my hair grow if you think it would help," Jim quipped, snapping his fingers and holding out an invisible straw hat. He jumped up, soft-shoed over to Catherine and tried to dance her away from the laundry.

Catherine giggled at the mock vaudevillian, but still she resisted his game. "Never mind, Jim, I have to get it done. Somehow, I even want to."

Life had sprung back for the moment to the days before, when they had adjusted to David, made allowances unaware. They did not know it then, but this day they began a new life, the life that David made.

Catherine shot sprays of starch on Danny's gray-striped shirt, then proceeded to roast and press it with the iron. "Aphasia," she thought, "has an important sound. 'My son suffers from aphasia.' " A valuable something she could drag out to show her friends. How could we survive without these words, these magic labels? "Aphasic David." She saw for a moment his mouth moving silently like a clumsy ventriloquist's, his words jerking forth unmatched to his expression as in a poorly synchronized movie. She heard his bleat, his yap, his sniff, his whine that never weeps. She saw his lips curved into a smile at something hidden from the world. "Oh, David, will they remember you're just a little child?"

CHAPTER THREE

Catherine had sprawled her body across the bed. She lay there dozing. The bedclothes were rumpled from a night of fitful sleep; the baby had wakened her twice in the darkness. In the corners of the room, dust affronted the icy eye of morning. David's pencil scratched on the window.

She had been rudely awakened from oblivion by the metallic sputter of the alarm. But waking had always been rude for Catherine. She slept deep. She wanted now to sleep forever in a tight, warm box of darkness. Alas, consciousness. It glowed like a miner's lamp into her cave of night.

She should be up, doing something, stopping him from doing that. She squeaked out, "David!" Maybe he'd come to bed and be cuddled. "David," she pleaded. "David," she whined. The pencil went on tapping on the window.

Too hard, this talking to a child who wouldn't listen, those eyes with no expression written on them. If only he would let her hug him the way he did when he was little. She would get up and tickle him. No, he wasn't even ticklish anymore. Pinch his bottom? Pounce on him from behind? He'd only pull away. Irked? No, not so much as panicked, as drowning, as crushing from some inner weight of silence.

Catherine rocked on her back moaning, lifting her eyes toward the shadows on the ceiling made dark by the rain clouds in the window. A cobweb hung wanly. She had given him more, she thought, than the other children. His presence never seemed to make her angry. He had caused no guilt, no threat. He reminded her of nothing that had hurt. She had polished white his little shoes, bounced him on the bed, ironed his diapers. She had been his mother.

Absolved momentarily, Catherine searched about for causes and for reasons. "The doctor," she mused. "He said the birth was

21

normal, but was it? He gave me so many drugs. I came too late, He said I came too late. The pains two minutes apart. Why," her guilt returned, "didn't I go sooner?"

"I bled the first month," Catherine made a ball head out of rolled sheet. "Why did he ignore it? 'Why,' what good is 'why?,' with him in there spitting on the window?"

Sure, the pediatrician had told her there was nothing wrong. And the psychologist had said there was, but "You two are doing all you can." Reality always stood in front of her, however much she cursed and stoned it off. David was getting worse. She knew it. Jim knew it. And by the time the Grand Poohbahs of medicine and psychology knew it and told it all innocent to her, it would be too late.

"Goddam," she cursed as the sun came slanting through the gray, nimbus morning; and her brain cells crackled and came alive. Always conscience, always guilt creeping out of its coffin box, genie-sized, accusing. Now, the unpardonable crime—the crime of apathy, of knowing and not doing, of self-pitying criminal inertia. David's bond to life, awareness . . . All men's bond to life, she saw it dying, bleeding from its pores like serum from a wound, and she not leaping up to staunch it. "A hemorrhage," she whispered at the blond hairs curling on the nape of David's neck, his head haloed in the window. There were tears in her eyes but she made her voice sound cheerful. "Look, David, I'll put ice cream on your cereal, and if you don't go in and eat it, Pooh-Bear will."

David heard his mother, but in a way a normal child hears a dog barking or a monkey chattering or a bird screeching. The tone beseeched, commanded a little. The sounds came separate and distinct. But there were no words.

Her tone, he wanted to please it, to answer the sad eyes that filled so often with disappointment. What must he do? Perhaps he would follow her and see what it was she wanted of him. His eyes told him so much more than they told others.

David placed his hands on the bear she held out to him and he followed his mother jabbering into the kitchen. "Eat, she wants me to eat," he thought, but not in words. Lifted into his high chair, he took his spoon.

"Ice cream," Catherine said as she plopped the roundish, white solid into his bowl "Ice cream," she kept repeating.

It did not occur to David to watch her face, to seek on her lips some clue to understanding. It would not occur to his mother to study a cat's lips for some subtlety of mewing. What nuances there were, were not perceived.

"Ice cream," Catherine persisted as David spooned the cold, white softness into his mouth with obvious enjoyment. His smiling eyes now passed across her face.

"Ice cream." David heard it a little different now as another child might hear a dog's growl as somehow different from his whine. Would his memory catch this distinction and hold it fast the way it held "Momma" and "Dadda" and "fish" and "hot"? The coldness would help it stick as would the color, the texture, the goodness of its taste. Perhaps "ice cream" would be remembered.

"It's not Greek," Catherine wanted to cry. "It's not a foreign language," her mind screeched impatiently. How much easier for David were it Greek! For if he had heard any language as another hears it, he would have known that it is words that are the key, that sounds have meaning, that thinking matches sounds, that sounds can be shaped to stand for feeling. He would have begun to know that words make ideas, make love, make virtue, make for humanness itself. Words are the chord on which humankind is struck. Words are all. All that matters. The rest is loneliness.

"Ahj." The sound popped into his mind suddenly. Was it not very like the sound she had been making? "Ahj," he thought, as his mouth made a crescent ringed with teeth. "Ahj," he whispered, and his ears marveled with recognition!

"Ahj." It shimmered on the silence. Catherine heard it. But did it have meaning? Indeed, was it meant to be a word? She watched her son with fingers in his ice cream.

"Ice cream," she said with clear enunciation.

"Ahj," heard David. "Could it be that she wants me to do 'ahj'?" The sound began swelling in his brain, escaping to his wonder through his mouth.

"Ahj" came that true, bright glimmer of a word. His eyes were shining with excitement.

"Ice cream," Catherine snapped with irritation. Is this the best you can do, she asked her sorrow. It had not occurred to her that David perceived sounds differently from other children or that his word might reflect his odd perception.

"Ice cream," she mumbled in frustration, having turned before she saw his looks of pride, passing David's effort without notice, leaving David's triumph without herald.

"Ahj" had been a word. The word that might have been In The Beginning. But no one heard.

Baby Maggie sucked her ten o'clock bottle in the kitchen on her mother's lap while David washed his hands in the ice cream. He stared blankly in the baby's direction as if her presence had drained his face of life. Smoke writhed from Catherine's cigarette, nose downward in the ash tray.

Then suddenly David was thrashing in his seat, wildly at first, and now with rhythm. Bleating, he beat his way toward the floor.

"What is it, David?," Catherine shrilled helplessly as his bowl struck the tiles on the kitchen floor and splintered into jagged bits of glass. "What is it? Christ, what is it?"

Maggie, startled and sprung erect, tore the nursing bottle from her mouth, seized a spoon and banged it on the table. David, kneeling now beside the high chair, beat his head with fury on the floor.

Tension crackled in the room like broken power lines.

"Stop it!" cried Catherine, bounding to her feet but driving Maggie's spoon into her cheek.

"Oh God!" She lifted the wailing infant to her face, "oh, God, what if it had been her eye!"

A scarlet welt blossomed on Maggie's cheek. Purplish nodes bloomed on David's brow.

"The broken glass!" Danger raced now through Catherine's mind as she watched her son edging towards the bits.

"Ay, ay, ay," came David's cry, the hammer of his heart beat in his eyes.

"Afraid, he's afraid," Catherine saw. Her heart jumped, not with *her* fear but with *his* . . . theirs.

And, taking in one arm her infant shaking with stifled sobs, and in the other her son in wrenching misery, she swept the glass underneath the chair with her foot, cooing, "It's all right, son," until he fell silent.

❋

Her old friend from the Art Institute, Martha Bester, had recommended Dr. Benjamin as "the best pediatric neurologist in the country" and Martha's husband was a psychiatrist and ought to know. But when Catherine called, the secretary made the earliest appointment for March. And this was December.

"Can't you make it any earlier?" Catherine had asked, suddenly impatient. David's "fits," as she called them privately—Jim said they weren't fits—had become more frequent as had his penchant for "windshield wiper," his strange, self-hypnotic game. At night her son never seemed to sleep. How often she would rise in the wee hours of the morning to feed the baby and would hear him chuckling and bouncing in the dark.

"Don't expect miracles," Jim had warned when she told him she was going to get an appointment. "Doctors are only people."

Catherine did not expect miracles but she hoped for one. She did not expect to take a frog into the office of the great man, and bring home with her a fairy prince. But she hit upon the idea of a pre-scription, a pill or a shot, something that would calm David and make him at the same time more voluble and wise.

Sometimes as she would lie there in the morning dreading to get up, her mind would fill with fantasy: of David growing up bright and beautiful; perhaps the principal, bald-headed, dressed in a vest and bowtie, making a special call at the house to exclaim on her son's intelligence; the coach, dark-jowled, virile, extolling David's fine sense of spirit in the field; David, winking at her knowingly; he, a person; they, two people sharing secrets; she, a mother, having called across the vast stretches of his wilderness, her son to home.

Other times, she would wake in anguish from terrible dreams: of David lying crushed and bleeding at a roadside, she pleading, "Let him live. At any cost, let him live." She could stand it. She could bear his yelps and bleatings, his stupors and rages, if he'd live.

"The best we can hope for is some sort of benign tumor, easily removed, or some pressure on the brain that can be eased," Jim spoke coldly that evening, after supper.

Catherine hated his stark, unsentimental vision of reality. "You don't believe in anything but yourself," she accused him with petulance. And then she felt secretly grateful he believed in that. God, too, she supposed Jim believed in God but it always seemed more important to him that God believe in him.

"Do you ever pray?" Catherine asked, suddenly curious.

"You mean, do I go around asking the Almighty to earn some-thing, to be worthy of my trust?" Jim answered over his evening paper.

Catherine smiled at his rhetorical question. No, she thought, You're too busy trying to earn His.

"Maybe there's a drug or something," she tried out her hope aloud. "Or some directions . . ."

She wants a recipe, thought Jim. He turned to her and put his paper down. "Catherine, the meeting with this Benjamin fellow is three months off. David is doing fine. Well, if not fine, the best that can be expected. I think you're building up to nothing."

"He's not doing fine. He smashed up Danny's model this morning."

"Danny shouldn't leave it around."

"And you know that neat little sailor suit my mother made him? He tore it to shreds . . . well, with his teeth."

"I know you haven't had a picnic, Honey," Jim began to reassure when their attention shifted to the kitchen.

Mark, Danny, and Jonathan had been playing Monopoly "quietly before you go to bed" when suddenly a scream came from their inner sanctum and a chair struck against the kitchen floor. Danny came bellowing to the parlor.

"If anybody's getting worse, it's Danny," Jim shot at Catherine before turning to his son. "For God's sake, Danny, what's wrong now?"

"They cheated!" Danny bawled at a distance no more than a foot from his father's ear. Tears flowed profusely down his cheeks.

"He broke up the game," Mark yelled, outraged. (Blessed are the martyrs and the saints!)

"Cheaters, cheaters, cheaters," Danny wailed.

"He broke up the game because he lost." Mark came crashing from the kitchen to set forth a spirited defense. Jon trailed him. He had a spark of the devil in his eye.

"Up!" Jim shouted, rising to his feet, his arm outstretched, his finger pointed upward like a lightning rod. "Up to bed, this instant, and no back talk!"

Danny, dark-haired, purple-eyed, shot the others a self-righteous glare and scurried up to bed. Jon, irked but submissive, followed in his wake.

"Why should we have to go to bed when *he* breaks up the game?" Mark shrilled with rising tears. "It's not fair," the eldest held his ground.

Jim raised his arm and gritted his teeth in menace, "Get to bed or I'll swat your behind, fair or not."

"There's no justice in this house," Mark in flight wailed over the top of the bannister. In frustration, he kicked the upstairs wall.

"Brat!" Jim muttered, surprising Catherine with his vehemence. "A lot of things are not fair. When was life ever fair?" He turned in his seat and hissed at his wife, "Well, is it?"

Catherine, who was trying to thread a needle, did not look up. Upstairs, anger continued to be exchanged, hushed but audible. David began rocking in his crib.

Jim stared at page 10 of *The New York Times* waiting for his ire to subside. Then it occurred to him that Catherine was angry too. Each time the boards creaked above them her jaw set and her breath heaved with irritation. The boys' voices up there quarreled in whispers. A sense of failure deepened round him. David was not fine but worse. Danny was doing poorly this year in school. "Shouldn't we," Catherine had asked that morning, "have a talk with his teacher, Mrs. Fellini?" He thought of the mop handle Catherine had smashed against the cellar wall. How she had said without emotion, "I can't stand it, Jim, anymore."

His wife sat, one seat on the couch removed from him, trying to put David's shirt together. She was thirty-four, her front curl the color of cigarette ash, the lines on her face began to deepen. Catherine had never been a a great housekeeper but now the dust balls gathered in the corners and the pictures hung crooked on the walls. Jim was moved by Catherine's strange, new aspect of fragility. She was someone of only human capacity with her own, secret limits of endurance. What would he do when those limits had been reached?

"Look, Jim, I'm just going to tell Fellini it's her problem and let her solve it," Catherine spoke airily, with mock confidence, as if she had read Jim's thoughts and understood his need for reassurance. "The kid's in the advanced class but she's got him believing he's going to fail . . ."

"I hope you told him . . ."

"Of course, I did," Catherine's voice skipped along as if she were apprising Jim of some item of local gossip. "I told him three times now: 'Look Danny, she can't fail you. Just do the best you can.' "

Jim was irked at the second-grade teacher's carrot-before-the-donkey style of teaching. Each time the child moved closer to the goal he believed she had set for him, she would move it just a little farther away. Danny had never been able to relish the satisfaction of accomplishment in Mrs. Fellini's class. Even when he did "A" work, his paper carried the notation: "This is not your best." Yet, somehow, Mrs. Fellini fully expected the child to sustain his attempts to spell and his efforts to read on these dashed anticipations of reward. Jim was a teacher too, and he knew better. But what to do?

"How did he do on the composition?" Jim asked.

"Last week's? Terrible. He started out: 'When I grow (spelled g-r-o) up, I want to be (spelled b-e-e) a paleontologist, (spelled correctly).' That's probably why she wants me to call."

Jim laughed. "She's worried about his spelling when he can spell 'paleontologist'?" Danny usually spelled phonetically, Jim mused, but of course, English was not phonetic. Perhaps he and Catherine could find time to teach him. . . .

"He came home from school crying yesterday," Catherine put in. "I was trying to listen to his problem but David kept beating his bell toy against the television set and I was afraid he'd smash it. Finally, it came out that she had told him he was so dumb, she wondered how he got into her class. I wish they'd drop him to the average group."

"They treat second-graders like they're freshman at Harvard," Jim spoke with rising anger. It would serve that teacher right if she had a class of Davids.

"I couldn't do a thing for him. He got so mad with David's incessant banging and my trying to stop him, Danny pushed David down, and David bit his own hand till it drew blood, and the screams woke up Maggie, and why go on?"

"It's her damn need to humiliate children." Jim's eyes glowed with little needle-points of light.

"She's nuts. We needn't take her seriously if Danny didn't. She tells me his W's are above the line. He doesn't write well, meaning his penmanship is poor. He doesn't pay attention meaning he's not thrilled to death."

"Christ," Jim thought, "will it never end?" Normal home life was out of the question for them now with David passing through some sort of crisis. But the school, did it have to create special problems, too? "Don't call her," Jim told Catherine with a sigh of futility. "Let her call you." Danny would have to fight it out alone. There was no strength left to "cooperate" in her terms. To hell with Mrs. Fellini, a hell full of brain-injured children.

"I told you Danny brought home a note today requesting I call Mrs. Fellini. I'm just going to lay it on the line: 'Sorry, my dear Mrs. Fellini, it's your problem.'"

"And for God's sake, don't get involved. You know. Be a little psychopathic." Now, he smiled. A planned maneuver made him feel less helpless. "Not angry, just a mite self-righteous. You know," Jim's voice was coated with rhetorical Vaseline, "Daniel never had this problem before, Mrs. F., not until they put him in *your* class."

"Daniel never had this problem before, Mrs. F.," Catherine echoed him. "Not until they placed him in your class."

"A little haughtier," Jim directed with arched eyebrows. "Don't beg. You sound like a streetwalker whining to the cops."

Catherine giggled. Looking straight ahead, she picked up an invisible telephone and listened with pretended concern.

"Uh, hum, yes, uh, hum," she nodded. "You say Daniel is not cooperative, does not pay attention in class." Her voice was molasses dripping in a barrel. "Quite the contrary, Mrs. Fellini, Daniel is positively intrigued . . ."

"By your peerless passion for the trivial," Jim interrupted. "He adventures forth each day," he crooned with a flourish of his arm, "with the unquenchable desire to find one, small violet of human interest beneath the avalanche of your niggling little molehills."

"Actually, Daniel loves school," Catherine tittered. Jim was flouncing around the room. "And we are surprised the compliment's not repaid . . ."

"Has he ever," Jim was crying, arm outstretched, right hand on heart, "thrown a dead cat in the teacher's room? Noticed your stupidity? Stolen your broom when he's missed the bus? My dear woman, surely a few W's above the line are a small price to pay for . . ."

"As parents we want you to know how grateful we are . . ." Catherine blurted.

" . . . for," Jim added with hands holding two unseen grateful hearts, "for the psychologist, the two social workers, and the psychiatrist with a specialty in dementia tremens who have kept you going all this time . . ."

And he and Catherine burst into laughter. Having thus disposed of Mrs. Fellini, they slept serene, like two Voodooites fresh out of pins.

＊

"Hi. What do you think of this?" Catherine asked with ill-concealed pride when Jim returned from work that evening. She sat at the kitchen table with David next to her. A cloth book lay open on the table.

"Smells great," Jim answered cautiously, pointing his nose toward the spaghetti sauce on the stove. He dropped his overcoat and briefcase on the kitchen tiles and poked a finger in the liquid. "Oo, that's hot!"

"Not that. This. Listen!" Catherine placed her hand over David's and made his finger point to a figure in the picture. "What's this?" she asked.

"Cow," David answered clearly. "Cow, cow." He seized the book in both hands and wrung it out like moist laundry.

"Great . . ."

"Shhh." Catherine pulled the book out of David's hands and fought him to lay it out on the table.

"Ehh," he began to cry.

She took his hand again and forced it on to another figure.

"Bucket," David cried "Bucket. Cow. Cow, bucket. Cow, bucket. Cow, bucket. Cow, bucket." He tried to tear the book but it wouldn't tear.

"I think its . . . ," Jim started.

"Now, wait, Jim." Catherine wrenched the cloth book back from David. She sped with it into another room. David shrieked. She returned in a second with two small plastic figurines, forced David down before them at the table.

"Cow, bucket. Cow, bucket," David, frantic, yelped as he snapped up the cow and bucket made of plastic. "Cow, bucket. Cow, bucket. He smashed them hard against the floor trying to break the cow.

"Great." Jim kissed Catherine, obviously delighted.

"Outstandingly ingenious, don't you think?"

"You're teaching him to generalize."

"Elementary, my dear Watson, elementary."

"Hey," Jim cried between munches of salted crackers, "those figures are terrific! *Were* terrific." Jim saw a broken bucket handle lying on the tiles beneath the table.

"The figures were pink. I painted them. You know, the Realistic School. It's okay. I bought and retouched five of each while Maggie and David were napping."

"Did he take a nap, you lucky . . ."

"More, a rock."

"Ay, ay, ay," David cried desperately. The amputated cow could no longer stand.

Catherine disappeared into the dining room-turned-fourth bedroom, and came back with a fresh pair of plastic figurines. "Listen, David," she said jokingly, "if you're going to be so destructive, you're not allowed to be so perfectionistic. Right, Daddy?"

"Right," Jim answered between sips of spaghetti sauce. "Well, Cath, looks like you've thought of everything."

"Not exactly." Catherine pulled the long strings of pasta out of the boiling water with a fork, and pitched them into an earthen bowl. "Here's the rub. He can't say 'cow' without 'bucket' and he can't say 'bucket' without 'cow.'" Catherine called toward the parlor, "Danny, come in and set the table, please, for dinner."

"That's easy. Separate them. The figurines, I mean."

"Did. Daniel," she shouted. "God, he's deaf. I tried it for about an hour. Half the time he screamed his head off. The rest of the time he was confused."

"Jim marched decisively into the bathroom and returned with a pink diaper bucket and placed it opposite David on the table. The smell of urine wafted over the dinner table. David struggled to get away.

"Umm, antipasto," Catherine chided.

"What's Dad doin'?" Danny asked. He began to pile the dishes across from David.

"This is a bucket," Jim said firmly. "This is a bucket, David."

David fought to get away.

"This is a bucket, David. Bucket."

"What's Dad doin', Mom?" Danny piled the silverware on the table.

"Bucket," David said clearly. "Bucket . . ."

"There, now," Jim began.

". . . Cow? Cow, bucket." David banged his head. "Cow, bucket, Cow, bucket. Cow?"

"Now that you have taught him to generalize," Jim cleared his throat authoritatively, "all you have to do is teach him not to put cow and bucket in the same category. Either that, or else you have to see to it that cows and buckets always appear together in his environment. A mere bagatelle. Tackle it tomorrow."

Catherine, in pretended disgust, set the sauce down on the table. "If you were any kind of husband, you'd buy a cow."

*

Sometimes when the other boys were drawing, David would snatch a piece of paper from their pile, purloin a pencil, and make his tight, close markings like wild grass. Jim was determined to teach him how to draw. It was a cold, quiet Sunday when Catherine spread her new green-and-white-checkered tablecloth over the kitchen table and, with skeptical confidence, said, "Oh, if only you could."

Jim neatly piled one corner of the table with the business section of the Sunday *Times* and placed the papers on top. Seated, David drew bunches of wild grass.

"Make a circle," Jim suggested cheerfully. "I mean a ball. David, make a ball."

David drew bunches of wild grass.

Gently, Jim took David's hand and made it move the pencil on the paper. First, an arc, now what looked like a flattened Gouda cheese.

"See, David, a ball," Jim declared in triumph.

David began to tense with rising fear.

Jim placed his hand on David's again. The arm resisted, but given the greater strength of the arm that moved it, it swung around again like a turning wheel.

The circle, itself, did not unman him. When Jonathan drew one, David was indifferent. It was the strange sensation in his arm, the sense of imbalance, the sense of his body doing something he didn't direct. Now his arm swept on to wider orbits, though all his being called on it to stop.

"Ay," David began to tremble. An image crept out of his ancient memory and formed a frightening picture on his mind. It was of the slanted world, his infant world, a world of solids that yield to weight like water, of surfaces as untenable as air. Unpredictable world, where, like bubbles, objects vanished with the reaching; like elevators' floors rose up and down.

David screamed. But Jim, who could not know why David struggled, kept him to the task he'd set for him. "David can make balls," said the father, resolved to ignore—for once—the fright so often with his child.

The sounds, the feelings they conveyed, might move David

toward this man some other time. But these were not his circles and the pencil was not an extension of himself. They had not been decreed by the central motor of his being, but by a competing turbine turning in his arm. Would his legs be next? Oh, terrible world of limbs one cannot trust!

David wrenched free of his father's hold and made circles on each piece of the paper pile. Frantically, without hesitancy, David's arm revolved. Over and over, the pencil cut through the sheets, then through the newsprint, down to the checkered cloth beneath. And now the circles eddied on the cloth uncoiling up, up, stringing out across the wall, a path of force across the room, compulsion blazing in its maker's eyes.

Then the unexpected happened. David suddenly gained control. The power surging through his arms and legs came under the dominion of his will. He could draw or not draw. At once, he had authority to choose.

"Stop," Jim was about to cry when David's line came writhing down the door frame, falling into loops as it went. But the line was trailing off into extinction. David sat down upon his leg, and his father silent, he watched the smoke curls from his cigarette drift up the world like the feel of peace.

The world rose around David, solid and symmetrical. His body weighed upon the unbent floor. The baseboards and the doorsills, both were defined. The cabinets had a disciplined design. Back into the silence slipped the phantoms of his fright. The world had not really changed at all!

A sense of freedom, David felt, the freedom to use his hands to draw. He had not wanted to draw a circle, but having drawn one, he felt unimprisoned to draw more. The motor of his arm had been spent upon the wall. It was the motor of his self that now would draw.

Then, to his father's wonder, David reached down and drew a circle, his own circle on the kitchen floor. Struck with the awe that befits a great event, Jim ran to summon Catherine to marvel too. Somehow David broke the casing of his fear, and in the breaking, he had not cracked the world.

"Ball," David thought with pride. He knew at last he'd pleased the ones he loved.

"Come here and let me hug you." His mother was crying joyfully. His father, festive, was beaming at the floor.

David smiled a smile almost forgotten. And his feet rose and fell upon his realm.

✳

The article about teaching young children to read had been clipped from the New Orleans *Times-Picayune*, and sent to Catherine by her father. It was obviously a fad, thus, something Catherine was determined to ignore. And, had she not been certain her father would ask her about it when she saw him again, she would have dumped each installment, of what turned out to be a series, in the trash.

At least ten clippings had arrived. Out of sheer annoyance, she read the first, and found it simply and convincingly written. The idea of teaching a young child how to read, particularly one in David's straits, struck a social acquaintance with his doctorate in education as "sheer hokum." A friend who was a student of psychology called it "inconsistent with everything we know about child development." Nevertheless, the next day, Catherine was resolved to teach David.

She spent most of Sunday evening measuring out spaces on poster paper for the eight-inch-high letters, erasing incessantly because "they should be perfect," painting and repainting, until "Mommy" shone forth in dazzling red.

"It's very simple. All you do is show him the card for three minutes at a time, five times a day," she explained to Jim, "And all you say is, 'This is Mommy.' Then, after showing him the card eight or nine times, you ask: 'David, what does this say?' And he says . . ."

"It's not reading, it's conditioning," Jim pontificated that morning during breakfast. But he spoke cheerfully. "Why knock it," he had been telling Dick Voorhees, the school psychologist, "Catherine is a lot easier to live with when she's saving the world than when she's judging it."

On the way to work, Jim felt guilty for having mocked Catherine's latest preoccupation. It was her way of fending off despair. And, besides, he enjoyed her sudden, unpredictable raptures of enthusiasm, her irrepressible pursuit of ideas she thought to be worthwhile. He recalled that when he kissed her good-bye that morning she had a certain vibrancy, a glow of the skin, a whiteness of eye, the arrogant pleasure of one who is truly alive.

He marveled at her sudden and passionate recoveries from

wretchedness, her intermittently determined search for potency, her full-moon tides of constructive energy, some highly creative, much uselessly spent, its rush through telephone wires, its flow through organizational outlets, its infusion of private projects, its insistence that some sign of hope surface for all to see. He feared her equally sudden eclipses, her crises in confidence, her dark-circled, leaden-eyed surrender to the near total darkness of defeat.

"If only this damn reading project would work," Jim was musing as his Ford turned off Route 17 and headed west toward Marsdale, New Jersey. "The David project," he muttered.

There were times and there was a level on which Catherine could abstract David into a project. Then, she would determine to read everything she could get her hands on that would in any way illuminate his condition, sending Jim on a weekly pilgrimage to the university library thirty miles away, poring over tomes on neurophysiology, trying to unriddle its mystery, wincing when Jim muttered about her "thumping grandiosity" and "we're not even sure what he has."

He would have been glad to help her decipher the neurology books, and he was not too humble to believe that he could. But he felt that at times the search for knowledge can be as sure an escape from reality as the cover of ignorance. Reading about brains would not help Catherine confront David. Coping with him would.

"David's not an abstraction, not to her anyway," Jim veered up Marsdale Avenue, thinking how the next time that idea came thundering in on her she'd be lying in bed late in the morning, crying for no apparent reason, performing the mechanics of her housewifely chores with shuffling disinterest, informing the human objects in her environment that unless they could shed some new light on David's condition they had lost their usefulness and roused her scorn.

"God, just let her teach him one word," Jim prayed as he rolled into the Marsdale Junior High School parking lot at 8:45, the very moment Catherine took out the card with the big red letters and began to unspin the cycle of her hope.

David thought his mother was playing "peek-a-boo" with the long white card with the strange, red markings. He looked at it and chuckled with expectation. She smiled and that encouraged him all the more.

"Momma," he heard. She held out the card and made "Momma"

with her mouth. David reached for the card, trying hard to pull it back. His mother held it tightly when he grabbed it.

She had always let him snatch the towel off her head when they played "peek-a-boo" in the bathroom. Why would she not allow him to do it now? He lurched for the card, this time with mounting anger. She made "Momma" again and again his momma smiled. Then, she put the card down and rolled with him on the floor. David began to enjoy the "Momma" game.

She played it two days, over and over, the way David liked it, she jumping and dancing and serving him ice cream and laughing the way he had not heard her laugh for a long, long time. And then she changed it so that he made "Momma" which he liked even better. He made "Momma" to his father, and his father clapped and sang and hugged him as he had not done when he played the game on the window.

One night when his mother was feeding the baby, he climbed up on his high chair, stood on its tray, found the "Momma" card on the top of the cabinet, and took it down. Later, he would hold it to him and stroke it in the gentle darkness, in the once warm silence that was growing cold.

For nearly two weeks, Catherine had been conditioning David to recognize first the word "Mommy" and then the word "Daddy" on her diligently lettered white cards. It appeared to her that for the first time David was able to focus for a fleeting moment on an object toward which he had been directed, a feat which she did not underrate.

Jim was more impressed by his son's waning desire to be alone. He did not believe David would learn to read, but he saw the "game" as a kind of counter-seduction to the siren song of his inner world.

To David, the game had become a point of contact like a light shining in the room of a child who wakes in darkness. Perplexed, disoriented, afraid, he must either lie trembling in the silence or charge forth to provoke the anger of his parents. For he is alone, estranged from them in their world of sleep. But then the light assures. It casts forth the outlines of a stable world, shadowy but familiar. It feeds back a presence beyond his own. It illumes an order to which he's briefly reunited, a reality to which he can belong.

"The real test comes tomorrow," Catherine was saying. "He

recognizes the 'Mommy' card and the 'Daddy' card. Now, if he can tell the difference between the two, he can read."

"Well, it's not exactly reading, Catherine," Jim put in. "But it's something pretty exciting just the same."

"But if he can tell the difference?"

"Oh, he'll be able to tell the difference all right," Jim shot Catherine a wicked glance. "The 'Mommy' card's the one with the slept-on look."

CHAPTER FOUR

The Stuyvesant Medical complex stood high on the back of the world. From mica-gleaming upthrust earth it rose. It was March and cold. The wind pounding from tower to tower, butting, breaking against its shocks of stone, hummed upon some hidden harp its awe.

"Dr. Benjamin?" the receptionist answered in clipped London-ese, "Eighth floor. Follow the red line to the lift."

Catherine and Jim looked at David and took the stairs. Elevators inspired fear. He could not bear the walls to move or the ground to rise. Catherine lifted David onto her husband's back and Jim jogged upward, his son like a heavy stone, his wife puffing, hacking from behind. "Damn cigarettes!" she said.

The corridor of the eighth floor, gray-marbled, smelled of steel and stone, slick magazines and odorless wood, nothing alive. Their footsteps clattered on the tiles like clicking heels. And beyond the sealed windows there loomed more proud towers, their lines athrob with the high charge of the world.

Catherine walked David down the long corridor. Then suddenly David stopped and looking up at a black sign bearing the legend "Doctor's Office," David cried, "Word! Word, word, word," he repeated, pointing, Catherine shouting encouragement in whispers, Jim coming from behind to mutter, "For God's sake pipe down, Catherine. They'll think *you're* the nut!" And she, still encased within her higher hope, rejoining, "I told you, Jim, once he could tell the 'Mommy' card from the 'Daddy' card, he'd read."

Jim was about to offer his, by now, classic distinction between reading and word recognition when Dr. Benjamin's secretary ap-peared at the door of his office to wave to them to enter the doc-tor's suite. The scent of the secretary's perfumed ear left its bouquet in the hallway.

"Ah David," the bull-necked man in the white jacket, having

turned out to be Dr. Benjamin, addressed their son. He loomed like
a pleasant mountain over his desk. "Come here, honey," his
strangely soft voice said.

David holding tight to a heavy metal hinge he somehow cher-
ished, backed up to avoid the doctor's proffered hand.

"It's all right, honey," the large man crooned. Then rousing his
ample frame up from his mahogany chair, like a great, pink bear
he lumbered across the room and placed a metal tape around
Catherine's head. "I'm only going to measure your mommy's
head."

The bear startled Catherine, no less David. A bleat of fear was
already in David's mouth when his lurching frame came down on
the doctor's desk, the sharp-edged hinge still in his hand.

"Ay," he yelped.

"Screeech," echoed the hinge.

The rose of anger spread round the doctor's smile. It appeared a
chip of mahogany had been gouged from the face of the doctor's
desk.

"What's he doing with that thing?" Benjamin cried. He scowled
at Jim, and Catherine blushed. Jim forced David down on his lap.

"I saw him in the hall," Dr. Benjamin suddenly confided without
looking at the measure of Catherine's head. "And I have a hunch
. . ."

Benjamin looped the tape around David's dome, checked and
rechecked the measurement he had made. It happened too quickly
for David to react. "He's three and he has the head of a nine-year-
old."

"But I have a large head, too." Catherine reoffered her head for
measurement. "And so does my son, Mark, and he's very bright."

Dr. Benjamin looked doubtful; but there was this woman's head
sticking out waiting to be remeasured. He complied with a grunt.
Then he motioned Jim to prepare to have his head measured, used
the tape and grunted again.

"You do have big heads," he said. He sat down behind his desk
and began to write.

"Take off his top clothes first," Benjamin directed. Jim began
straightway to peel off the layers of elegance Catherine had put
on: the handsome sports jacket, the red suspenders, the brown tie,
and the crisp white shirt. "College of St. Joseph" emerged on his
underwear.

This time Jim blushed. "Hmmph, Catherine," her humor taxed him.

David wanted to run out into the corridor leaving his clothing, his mother, his father and the big bear behind. But the bear was on top of him again with rubber ropes attached to a metal disk, an ice cube in communion with his heart.

"It's all right, honey," Dr. Benjamin said absent-mindedly, holding up David's left arm and trying to get it to drop. It rocked to and fro like a lever. "Pretty rigid."

David felt a spasm in the center of his gut. But then the doctor tickled his feet; and when he brought a hammer to strike him on the legs, the hammer intrigued him. He thought of striking back.

"Take it, Dave," the big man commanded. "But, not on the desk!"

The small boy snatched the hammer quickly, raised it and brought it down on his own knee. He shrieked silently. His eyes were lit with pain as he fell upon his knees. He struck and restruck his head on the carpeted floor.

"Get up, hon," the doctor said anxiously as Jim rose to the rescue. Placing a paper under the banging head and forcing a pencil into David's hand, he waited for his son to draw a circle. He drew only bunches of wild grass.

"Was the birth normal?" Benjamin was wearing his glasses now, two little moons on the mountain behind his desk. "Any complications? Normal?" He looked up.

"Normal pregnancy, normal delivery, normal birth. Everything was normal," Catherine answered finally. "Except David, of course." She had prepared a two-and-a-half-page history of David from birth to thirty-eight months, covering everything from feeding to socialization. It was sitting before Dr. Benjamin on his desk.

She had written it as a kind of brief, an argument for David's abnormality, a proof against the glib reassertion that "lots of children talk late," or "you two are doing the best you can." But secretly she had also prepared it in hopes that the doctor would rise to her son's defense, that he would strike down each damning jot of evidence, that he would find the culprit lurking somewhere else.

The endless questioning went on. She recalled how she had had to teach him to eat a cookie, how he had always been afraid of falling, how he had tried desperately to speak and failed, how he had withdrawn into his private world and ticked away in silence on the window.

Benjamin winced visibly when Jim used the word "autistic" to describe David's recently acquired mannerisms. He was not impressed, he said, "with psychodynamic explanations." He preferred to see the brain from "its physical side."

"We're going to get an E.E.G. on him and a skull X-ray and we're going to find out what he's got and see what we can do to correct it."

Catherine came suddenly to life. The doctor spoke as if he were assuming responsibility for David's condition. Was the burden of directing her son's life then to be his, not hers?

"Frankly, I think he has arrested hydrocephaly." The neurologist exuded confidence. "It's just a hunch based on that big head, but . . ."

"Hydrocephalus?" Jim asked.

"Well, it's just a hunch . . . One thing's certain though, he's brain-injured. The signs are gross. That psychologist's report you handed me greatly underestimates the damage. At least as far as I can tell."

"Is it his reflexes?"

"No, it's his behavior, the head size. The motor damage is very slight. But from the history your wife gave me . . ."

It was then not just a passing phase, David's strange behavior. Catherine knew now that it was here to stay. The truth that had lain there in the dark, that spoke into her lonely meditations its silent and its ominous predictions, was not a ghost. It burst into the daylight—real, substantial, unimagined. The doctor had seen it with his own eyes, with his heightened perception, with nothing to gain or lose by his point of view.

Their worst fears had been confirmed, yet Catherine and Jim felt strangely relieved. It was the present that concerned them. They had not learned to fear the future. For the moment, the doctor's verdict served to restore confidence in the evidence of their senses, ay, even here where their own child was involved. There's enormous safety in being able to trust one's own vision of reality, however terrifying that reality might be. Catherine and Jim looked at one another, the realization having come to them at once. It is given to those who can trust what they have seen to search for a way to understand. Meaning is, perhaps, all there is to life.

Dr. Benjamin did not know what to make of the Fitzgeralds, especially Catherine. He had given them what other parents called "a life sentence" and the father had not paused nor the mother wept. Mrs. Fitzgerald had only turned for a moment toward the window but now remet his gaze with no sign in her eye. Four children and this one, he thought. Perhaps it's different when you divide your love five ways. He thought of his own two children. The senses numb, you don't worry so much how each one gets through life.

Still they seemed bright and they seemed to love the child. The mother's history had been literate and thoughtful. Perhaps they had not understood.

"If it is hydrocephaly, and I think it is, even an operation would leave a residue of mental deficiency . . ."

They nodded as if they already knew.

"Frankly," Benjamin confessed finally, "I don't understand your reaction or rather your lack of one." His voice seemed to surprise him. He wiggled uncomfortably in his seat.

Catherine looked up from a list of questions she had prepared for the occasion. The neurologist's eyes fled hers. He was embarrassed. Had he expected her to scream or faint or what? If she had not yielded to such things when she and Jim were alone with the problem, why would she now when the doctor had promised to give them help?

"We knew that if there wasn't something very wrong with him," Jim explained, "there had to be something very wrong with us."

"We live with him," Catherine protested. Did he think he only behaved that way in the office?

"I think you must be a good mother," Benjamin put in apologetically. If they had not come to him for diagnosis, why had they come? "Fluid circulation can sometimes be restored," he told himself. "But the best they can hope for is a moron. That I can't correct. But surely they must know . . ."

"I mean I think you're the kind of woman who can live with the fact that brain tissue cannot be restored," Dr. Benjamin said.

A good mother? Catherine hoped that it was true. Her own mother was the prototype, and she was a perfectionist, so much better than her daughter, a perfect housekeeper, a perfect recipient of psychological advice from the pamphlets of Metropolitan Life.

"But brain-injured children can be helped," Catherine asked almost rhetorically. She would be the perfect follower of directions. The doctor could demand heroic sacrifice. She would do what he should ask no matter what. "Tell me," her eyes inquired, "What must I do?" "As soon as we have the results of the skull X-ray and the E.E.G., we'll see to it," Benjamin returned to his confident bedside manner.

Jim heard the neurologist telling Catherine that the drugs he wrote down on his prescription form "were sure to help, you see, dexedrine has the reverse effect on children." He seemed to be trying to tell her that David would never be normal, that his condition could never be "corrected" in the sense she understood, and yet he let her believe that he could set it right. Catherine could bear the truth, Jim knew, if fantasy were not made too seductive.

"I know he can learn," Catherine spoke now of her experiments in 'reading.' "He already recognizes the difference between one set of symbols and another . . ." Her voice went trailing off. Dr. Benjamin stopped her chatter with a scowl.

There was a storm on the mountain that rose over the dark, mahogany desk. Brush fires blazed in the doctor's eyes. "Mrs. Fitzgerald," he glared as if he recognized at long last who she was. She was the mother who when told her son could never play the violin had to rush out and sign him up for lessons. She was the driver, the bully, the whip. "Mrs. Fitzgerald," he growled, "you don't seem to understand. Your son has a serious organic problem. It's absurd for you to teach him how to read."

✳

On the way home, Catherine did not speak. She said she was trying to integrate what Benjamin had told her into some kind of message. Jim seemed testier than usual over the traffic clogs so common in New York. David with the joy of one reprieved bounced on the back seat of the Ford.

Then from the deep chasms of the city choked with gas, they broke out into the sky, the Bridge spreading over them like the net of the Fisherman. Into the web of the world they did glide, it steel-spun and sun-bedazzled, its thrusts belittling the mountains, its arch soaring to the joys of grief. Together and inside them, the fire sank. Gradually, faintly, delicately. But knowing nothing yet of fires, David laughed.

CHAPTER FIVE

Catherine opened one eye and shut it again. David was at the window making an arc in its sweat. "Tick, tick tick," David was marking every moment that passed without hope into the next.

Catherine pulled the covers up over her head. She wanted to hide. Outside the wind wailed but it could not sing her into sleep. Now she tore the covers off and stared across the room at the silent figure.

Hope, with its spark in the heart, its spangle in the eye, had gone from him, leaving him apart from her. She watched his impassive profile, the slight flicker of his dulled eye. Was this what life meant from now on—utter, intact separateness? Perhaps this was all he had been, the flat imitation of a human child, his strangeness obscured by the heat of her own hope.

In dread she turned her face away. Each time she had embraced him there had been nothing between them, yet she had embraced him repeatedly, loved him, called him "son." She looked at him now, her spirit cold and detached, saying clearly: "What have I been doing all this time? Loving a child who did not exist? This other one existed all the time."

Tears welled in Catherine's eyes. She felt for the first time the utter isolation of the human soul. Hope had died in her son, she knew, because it had died in her. She taught him no more words, gave him no pencil with which to draw, showed him no pictures, did not interrupt his silence. His speechless call for help must go unheeded. Nor did she wish it any other way.

The draperies that surrounded the misted window where he stood were caked with dust. The sheets were gray with ancient wrinkles. And from the kitchen there rang the drip, drip, drip of a broken faucet. Were it not for the infant's cry every few hours, she would not have risen from her bed. For having lost faith in the possibility of David's recovery she had lost faith in life.

It had taken her three days for Dr. Benjamin's message to sink in. And even then Jim had had to make it clear to her.

"He only told us what we already know, Catherine," Jim had said. "We knew he was brain-damaged. We knew brain cells don't regenerate. He was supposed to be the objective source who confirmed what we had already come to, what's become clearer and clearer over the past year, what we live with every day: David is not like other children."

"But he said he could correct it," she had persisted. "He implied that he could make him well."

"Not well, Catherine. He meant that he could keep him from getting worse. Did you seriously think a neurologist could remove brain damage like an appendix? If David has this hydrocephalus— and, frankly, on that point, I think Benjamin's up a tree—he could maybe drain some of the excess fluid out of the hollows in David's brain to keep it from destroying healthy tissue. But he can't restore what's lost. Look, Honey, you know that yourself. Remember Merritt's book or was it *The Living Brain?* You're the one who kept quoting the stuff to me."

"You mean he's always going to be like this, when he's six or sixteen or thirty-six?" Catherine had then begun to cry. "You mean he'll never be like us, be a person?"

"There's a person in there all right," Jim had answered hollowly. "Someone we don't really know. And there are ways . . ."

It was true. Catherine had known for a long time that David was not like other children. But hope springs from trust in the some-day, from the belief that what is needed can somehow be attained. Catherine needed David to get well, not immediately, but someday.

Jim had said that there were things that she could do. But if nothing could bring about David's recovery, if everything would still leave him incomplete, what use were they? The future stretched before her, indeterminate, without goals, for the one goal of David's normality had been denied. Catherine was the child who wakes in the blackness, who shrinks from the terror of the endless, the unbroken line of the dark.

Jim had skipped the teachers' salary meeting that Thursday even though he knew too well he was the teachers' most forceful and persistent agitator. The Ford had turned onto Summit Street and he had already prepared a smile of greeting when Catherine, in the eighth house from the corner, began to ascend the stairs. He shouted a cheerful "Hi" to Danny wrestling on the grass with his good friend, Bob, even as Catherine reached the pinnacle of the staircase. Pretty soon the jonquils, he told himself as he passed the seedbed by the porch, pushed open the front door, and instinctively felt a presence there above him. He wheeled before his mind told him anything, and leaping up the stairs, he found Catherine standing at the window.

"Catherine!" he shouted in a voice sick with fright. "Catherine, my God, what are you doing?"

She turned toward him dumbly as if his voice had come from the center of a fog. "I came up to get the baby," came her strangely metallic reply. "It looks like she's fallen back to sleep."

A few minutes later in the kitchen below, she counted six potatoes for their supper. Beside her feet, David was lying on the floor. Upstairs, Jim was nailing in the windows.

✳

Before he left for work the next morning, Jim went into the bedroom and kissed Catherine lightly on the cheek. Her hair was rumpled, her eyes closed. She pretended to be still asleep. The boys had gone bellowing forth to school, hair slicked down, pants neatly creased. It was Jim who had roused them and packed them off. Could she not now rise to this small ritual of affection? Irked, he stalked out of the bedroom, through the kitchen, parlor, doorway, slamming every door as he passed. The Ford sprang like a lion into Summit Street.

Jim did not know whether Catherine was sick or not. He was sure that she wanted to be. She wanted to substitute some other reality for the one she could not bear. Would she succeed? His days were taken up with wondering.

And with anger. "God," he shouted as the match he struck to light his morning cigarette seared his fingertip instead. "God," he repeated scornfully, "helps those who help themselves."

A man who had never been inclined to seek help himself, Jim saw nothing strange in a God who only gave help when it wasn't needed. Did Catherine need help? He rejected the question before it came fully into mind. For he did not know for certain how to give it.

He had tried to help her, he thought, as the car turned west on the winding road that lead to the highway. He had asked, even insisted, that Catherine and he go out to dinner, to a movie, to visit friends. But he was too tired, too depressed, too burdened with work, she said. She preferred to be imprisoned in the darkness.

Jim waited for the light to change on Route 17. He watched the cars flit by paced by human beings who wished and hoped as once he and Catherine had wished and hoped together. He felt deeply alone. That sense of oneness, the thing he had shared with Catherine had nearly vanished. She—her damn self-pity—had turned away. If she awaited him at all, it was with silent anger. There was no gift of grace he could bestow.

He's my son, too, his mind nearly howled as the Ford thundered south along the highway. Couldn't Catherine see that a part of the pain in him was joined to the pain in her? She was the pivot of their private world, the keeper of the idiom of their union. Was it not possible for her to care, to be impelled toward the future by her caring?

Rolling into the Marsdale lot, Jim set his jaw and prepared to assume his role. He was compelled to hope even if it must be a private, lonely act. It is not possible to despair with someone else.

*

April poured the colors of the rainbow on the world and the drops on the glass were shot with silver. Through his window, David saw the new house nearly risen, the green daggers of the new grass, the scrambled-eggs blossoms of forsythia. He did not smile. There was something in the richness that he feared, the way it battered on his senses. He preferred the stern, the iron-colored earth, the metal sky. The play of colors in the oil slick on the road was all the rainbow he could bear.

He feared this chaos, spring, the waking, altering, surging flow of life, the way it rushed his senses as if to make them join. It engulfed him like an over-friendly sea, lifting, hurling, pounding, making deaf and blind, mixing brutality with love. He made himself as senseless as a rock, and hid from its caresses on the shore.

David had not thought for a long time, nor had he felt. Neither had he wished for he no longer had a sense of what could be. He tuned down his eyes and ears, velveted his fingertips, listened to the gurgles of his heart. He would open his ears to the whistle of a train, his eyes to the spinning of a top, his fingertips to a string tied to a key. He could jiggle, rock, make the truck wheels spin. Beyond that, the limits of his inner space reached out to be the limits of the world.

There was no contact with the people out there, the same ones with the same names, and the same faces, only now like creatures in a dream, eating, opening a window, making their mouths move, filling space. He avoided their eyes.

He longed for time to stand still, for space to become obedient. This chair must not move. The clock must not dismiss the present moment. There must be no change, no chink of light within the tomb, no tear, no smile, no claim that joy and gloom are not the same, no dead wish yearning to be reborn.

Catherine was afraid of pain but more afraid of silence. For no nightmare held the terrors of the silence she now knew. And her son knew it better. This child like all young children had not yet grown inward, found no point in the midst of the indeterminate that was his and his alone. But this child unlike the other children was damned to never grow, she mused, never find, yet damned to live. And to live in silence. Only a stone is stopped at the limits of the present. Even mountains rise. Rivers are not still. Trees and flowers indignant with their one dimension struggle toward the sun. But this child? Could it be that this child, dulled, damned, speechless but still the facsimile of genius was less than these? Catherine wondered.

He had been like other children once. His brain had been adequate to infancy, to babyhood. Some message folded in his brain's crypt was unfolding then. Where had it vanished? Or was it vanished? Jim had told her that she must have faith. Faith in what? One can have faith in illusion. In herself? "In me?" she cried, turning towards the ghost at the window towards the child she had deserted in his need. She wept without self-pity for she knew the extent of her guilt. In God?

Catherine pushed aside the gray sheets, arose, went to the dresser spotted with spilled perfume, searched the upper drawer, found the entreaty that begins: "Out of the depths I have cried to thee, O Lord." She read it standing, stepped, sat, read it once again, feeling no transparent light, no thrust of faith to pierce the will, the mind, the spirit, soul. She heard, barely, but she heard the helplessness, all minds in which the world is conscious joined to weep, all there in one forsaken cry, all lost, all raging in the dark.

Catherine rose and walked to David, knelt and squeezed his body in her arms. She forgave, not the child but herself, patted him, tried to see his eyes, spun a top, chose to be human in the dark.

She stayed that way, holding David's unresponsive body in her arms for a long time waiting. Then, at last, an idea came to her and she rose, pulled the poster paper out from behind the couch and laid it out on the kitchen table.

"Now where's that darn construction paper?" she said aloud as she rummaged through the junk in the kitchen cabinets. "Aha," she beamed as the pack was uncovered. She took a red piece from the pack and began to draw. First a triangle. She cut it out, placed it on the poster paper, and traced around it. Next a circle. Finally a square. Within a half-hour, Catherine had constructed a simple game. The object was for David to place the appropriate figure— circle, triangle, square—on the matching outline on the poster paper.

Not exactly ingenious, Catherine said to herself, but something. Hope had begun to come to life in her. She saw that it could not be sustained unless it were anchored in something concrete. There had to be some frame, however narrow, in which she could operate. There had to be something practical she could do.

"David," she called. "David!"

To her surprise, David emerged from the bedroom.

"Come here," she sang. "Look at the game your mommy made for you."

David moved closer, his eyes falling on the bright, red patterns. Catherine knew enough not to be direct. She took up the triangle first, glancing sideways at her son, and with noisy exclamations of amusement, set it down on top of its counterpart.

"Marvelous! What a marvelous game," she chirruped as she picked up the circle. She suppressed an urge to ask, Do you want to try?

There was no need. His response was instantaneous. He snatched up the square, elbowed his mother away from the poster paper and placed the square atop the square.

Catherine grabbed David, laughed, danced out a wild flurry of delight over David's accomplishment. But David would have none of it. He took up the triangle that had fallen off the paper and pushed it until it fit exactly with the triangle it matched. Wasting no time, he found the circle and placed it right where it should go. Then, he dumped the figures off the paper and began the process of matching once again.

His mother's exaggerated plaudits had no effect on him. She

might have been the radio, his brothers playing, the extraneous noises from the street. It was not her sentiment David required but her life force; it is not love so much that the fetus requires as the cord that feeds and binds. His communion with life through her set him free; free to somehow, somewhere, on the panes of the window, on the pockmarked walls, with a piece of plain red paper, to vent his passion to achieve.

David matched the figures time after time, turning to his mother with a look that cried for more. He reached for the cards that used to be kept on top of the refrigerator, and Catherine, searching frantically, found and showed them, David choosing "Mommy" from "Daddy" at once. Triumphant, he called them out over and over again. Then once more he was searching. And his mother, acting on his ardor, dashed about finding buttons to sort, paper for drawing circles, blocks to pile, until, at last, Maggie sounded forth for her bottle, and David retired to his crib.

Catherine sat feeding Maggie and trying to assess what had occurred. It seemed to her, though she could not as yet be certain, that David had shown forth his peculiar strength, a strength greater than any she had found in her other children. His was a rage to learn, a passion to overcome, some obscure organic choice to grow. It was as if her son were driven by human contact to explore, forced to seek, compelled to find his own particular horizons. Denied the Word, denied perhaps the thought that coincides, David had to have his hand upon the work. He had to mark existence with some sign or hammer down his spirit in the silence.

Catherine no longer felt the sense of separation from her son she had felt before. As long as their two worlds touched, they could learn from each other. For if she remained intact she could wait at the door that is not yet open.

"No, we don't have to adjust to reality all at once," Jim was saying that evening after supper. "We don't even know in David's case what reality is."

"Just the same," Catherine shot back, "all the manuals say 'Adjust to the child's situation as it really is.' Of course, they don't say how to do it."

Jim sat stuffing himself with Catherine's "Jewish lasagna"— "Jewish" because it was made with sour cream. "What a dinner!" he chuckled aloud, the first elaborate meal since Dr. Benjamin. He felt giddy with relief.

"It's one thing to adjust to a certainty, and another to adjust to a likelihood," he heard himself saying. "I mean that it's likely that David is abnormal though we are not at all certain he always will be."

Jim had dared not despair and so he had dared not feel. In a sense, Catherine had deserted, leaving him lucid and in charge.

His wife sucked her teeth in annoyance. "We know he's abnormal. Jim, if you start giving me that Jesuit logic stuff again, I swear I'll scream."

She was right of course. There was no longer any need for it. He was free now; free to pity her isolation, free to fear she might've taken her life, free to be afraid his son was lost. He was free to give them both the help they needed, which on the most desperate level, they didn't need anymore.

"Look!" Jim yelled, letting himself get testy. "All I'm saying is that David may not be permanently impaired so there's no point in our adjusting ourselves to a permanent impairment if there's a good chance it doesn't exist."

"What about this unregenerated brain tissue business?" Catherine had accepted David's brain damage only on the most superficial level. Still she was wary of false hope.

"I hear there's a way to get around it."

"For Gosh sakes, Jim, we're talking about a brain, not a legal contract."

"I'm aware of that." Jim dabbed at a splash of tomato sauce that had fallen on his tie. "Ever hear of Sister Kenny? She had this supposedly kooky theory about building new pathways to the brain, and everybody laughed until it worked."

"Dr. Benjamin doesn't sound like he has any truck with new pathways to me. Who's going to tell us how to build them?"

"We are." Jim bubbled with confidence. "We're going to work with him," he said zealously. "We're going to teach him. We're not going to give up the words, or the drawing or the cows and the buckets."

"No matter what Benjamin . . . How well I know he needs it. He craves it, like water or food," Catherine laughed, "like dope."

"David is going to be our guide." Jim announced the strategy for the future. "David and our own sense of reality. We know him better than anyone else. We know we can trust what we see. Now we're going to have the guts to act on it."

"But what about the rocking? What about the scraping on the window? Can we deal with that?" Would they have to be their own best last resource?

Jim brought his face up close to Catherine so that their noses nearly touched. "You know the answer to that yourself," he said sadly. "Somehow we've got to deal with it. If he were drowning, we wouldn't dare wait and hope for help to come along. We'd dive in and struggle the best we could."

"But I don't know how to . . ."

"You've already begun. You've known instinctively that whatever breaks his contact with the world . . ."

"Then we'll have to stop the drugs," Catherine said firmly. "They only make him glassy-eyed and dull."

"OK, we'll stop them." Jim spoke slowly as if awed by his own words. "We'll do what we must do." Quietly, he brushed the crumbs off the tablecloth into his hand and thought aloud. "Reality is like air to him," he said.

"Yes, like air," agreed Catherine. "He needs it."

❊

Miss Martin, the school nurse, called next day in the midafternoon. She had a lilt in her voice and a genuine affection. The boys amused her. Jonathan was "so cute," Mark "a worried old man," Daniel "strapping." Catherine pictured her, the amused eyes, the tilted nose, her compliments falling on Catherine's children like warm raindrops.

"Mrs. Fitzgerald, were you aware that Daniel has trouble with his eyes?"

They had been chatting casually. The question took Catherine by surprise.

"What kind of trouble?"

"Well, we gave him the yearly eye checkup today and he did very poorly. He has something like 20/200 vision in his left eye." Miss Martin's voice sounded serious, somewhat disturbed.

"I had no idea," Catherine answered. The image of her second-born flooded her consciousness: Danny with the uncombed hair, eyes more indigo than blue.

"Of course, 20/200 is quite bad, Mrs. Fitzgerald. It's the border-line between sight and blindness. It means a person sees an object at 20 feet as if it were 200 feet away. I thought you'd want to get him checked by an ophthamologist."

"Are you certain?" Catherine had never seen him squint. He sketched with gusto, and symmetry and dimension. "I mean he draws well, I haven't seen any sign. There was nothing wrong with his vision last year."

Another one, another failure, Catherine thought. More disorder in the chaos of their lives, more to mute the kindness of the heart.

"We tested him twice. I'm sorry. I hope it all works out."

The phone clicked and then was silent.

Jim had called Catherine a few minutes later. He had asked her if she needed anything from the store, something he might pick up on his way home from work. It was just an excuse. He had wondered how she was. Her voice sounded dull again, without its newfound life as she related her dialogue with Miss Martin. His reponse had been cheerful, comforting, and false.

The other children, Jim mused on the way home, how easy it was to forget the other children. Of course they had problems. All children do. Jim thought of their broken airplanes, his broken promises, their safe world broken now by change. How were they taking it? It had not occurred to him for a long time. Could they live on the minimal care, concern, joy, Catherine and he had lately given? Could you ask children to live by candlelight until their parents crawled out of the dark?

They had tried to explain to the children the nature of David's problem, why David smashed their model ships, how come he ruined their outing at the zoo. They had listened with interest but hardly with understanding. How could they react? Like the sweet little darlings in fiction? "I don't care anymore if I win at Monopoly, Mother, my needs are too trivial for concern." Or, "I shan't go blind in my left eye this month, Mother and Dad couldn't bear it."

As he crossed the highway and turned north and east toward home, it occurred to him how much easier life might be if they denied David's impairment and let him rock in silence in his crib. But up the hill, past the fruit stand with the trained skunk, the rain swirled on his windshield, and shot through the vent like tepid tears. He thought of David alone at the window, mocking these very pendulums, hearing his strange music, while the other boys laughed, sang, joked, fought, clung to each other, filled themselves with purpose, dreams, desires. "Keep strong," he counseled. And the sky wept endlessly around him.

✳

Children's Hospital did not smell of children. It was disinfected to
the bone, dreary, monotonous, tooled with nothing to delight the
childish eye. Two Victorian cherubs with wax fruit cheeks smiled
dully from the wall. Outside the wind worried the winds and the
April showers sputtered on the windows.

"That'd be X ray, fourth floor," the receptionist looked up for a
moment from her long layers of Pliofilmed cards and smiled tautly.
"Follow the red line to the elevator, left!"

Catherine, Jim, and David pressed through a room filled with a
redundance of humanity. Short, sallow people standing, babies in
arms, their garments dripping with rain; tall Negroes; a fat mulatto
with a hacking infant, its cheeks bulging like a puffin's, a teardrop
hanging from its nose; a small boy with a stiffening upper lip. They
stood there like pigs in a packing house waiting for their white
cards to be stamped.

People-studded rooms made David queasy. Catherine pushed
him quickly through a door marked "Exit," and they began their
ascent up the concrete stairs.

"Time?" Catherine puffed.

"Nine twenty-nine," Jim answered. "We ought to hit the half
hour on the nose."

The nurse in charge was an executive, floating power, elbow-
action, find-your-name-in-a-second type, who said "Fitzgerald,
David, nine-thirty. Undress him in the dressing room, 403, all
except the underpants, and wait."

They obeyed. The clock ticked on and on while they wrestled
with his shirt, his screams, his shoes, his cries, his pants. He struck
out with a vengeance at *Life* magazine, broke the spring on his
wind-up baby his mother brought along, ate seven lollipops with a
chomp. Then half an hour later they were called.

"Just one parent. You." The pink-faced Irish nurse's aide
pointed unmistakably to Jim. "The mothers often cry when the
child starts screaming."

Without a word Jim was up dragging, tugging, toting David
down the long gray marble corridor, Catherine watching while her
son tried to cover his nudity like a modest asthenic at the beach.
Then a young man in a white coat seized David, rushed him
through a door, leaving Jim standing in the hallway. Jim waved
weakly to his wife.

Soon screams flowed up the corridor and down, climbing and diving, drowning the shuffle of nurses and the rain. Jim paced to and fro and Catherine turned away so she wouldn't see him. Then suddenly David reemerged in Jim's arms sobbing and Jim plus David came charging up the hall, keeping pace with the doctor wearing glasses.

"What do you mean, you can't do the X ray?" Jim was demanding. "You've got to. We've got to eliminate hydrocephalus."

The bespectacled doctor mumbled his response.

"Of course he won't lie down under that thing," Jim was talking at the top of his voice. "If he were the kind of kid who just up and lies down under strange machines," her husband sounded angry, "we wouldn't have had to bring him here in the first place."

The radiologist muttered something else.

"Look, my wife will hold his arms, and I'll hold his legs . . ."

"Mumble, mumble, mumble, it's the rules." The doctor vanished through a doorway.

Jim stood there, David still in his arms, waiting. "Down the rabbit hole," he cursed, and turned away.

"Jim," Catherine called. "Jim," she called again, "don't you think we'd better go?"

"Not on your life," he cried. Marching over to the young man in the white jacket, he told him calmly, "I'm sure my wife and I can get him to . . ."

"It's against the rules," said the man, and he walked away.

"What's this, a crazy house?" Jim demanded of Catherine. "Just because David won't lie down under that X-ray machine without resisting, they won't do the X ray. I mean what three-year-old kid in his right mind or his wrong mind either is going to . . .?"

"Baby gun," David cried. "Baby gun."

A little girl, her face distorted as if reflected in a pool, lay on a stretcher. They wheeled her into the X-ray room in silence. Catherine and Jim watched her roll inside.

"Baby gun," David said.

"Listen," Catherine cried cheerfully, "David thinks the X ray is a baby gun. What's it like? Do they have it disguised to look like an elephant or something?"

"Chrissake no." Jim flopped down on the sofa in the dressing room. "Just because they call this morgue 'Children's Hospital' doesn't mean they've got a damn thing here for children. It's just a great, big, shiny machine with a mirror and a slab and straps. And it sounds like a meat grinder. It would give an adult a nightmare."

They turned to the sound from the door, rose and watched the girl come wheeling out.

"Probably a tumor case," Jim said. "They get lethargic when they've got a tumor."

"Well," Catherine tried being pleasant, "at least we know he hasn't got a tumor."

"Cripes," Jim shot back angrily, "they ought to call this place 'Tumor Hospital.' They can only X-ray tumors. Everything else is against the rules."

Catherine picked up David's shirt and began to dress him.

"You can dress him so he doesn't get a cold," Jim remarked. "But we're not leaving."

"But I thought you said . . ."

"Are you crazy too?" Jim was still boiling. "Are we going to go through all this again? Is he going to be any better tomorrow, next week, or the week after? Are they going to be any better?"

"What'll we do?" Catherine was asking when Jim disappeared into the office of the efficient nurse and her voice cut coldly through the din.

"They're calling Benjamin for a sedative . . ." Jim wheeled back into the dressing room.

"I know, I heard . . . What now?"

"Now," Jim leaned back as if he were about to take a nap, "now we stage a sit-in."

Catherine had never known Jim to be so determined. He was too, well, civilized in general, she reflected, to demand victory. This time, clearly, he had to win. Worry and defeat were all around him: concern for her, worry for the children they feared they had neglected, fears about their son maimed by the brute energies of Nature—blind but overpowering.

They had begun to make small conquests over themselves, Catherine mused, ones she knew—alas—a few unproductive weeks with David could easily reverse. They had begun to create plans and programs to offset the accidental malice of the world. Now, another frustration equally blind, purposeless, stupidly inhuman! Jim had to pit his puny but purposeful power against the Goliath Routine of the hospital.

A few hours after the call to Dr. Benjamin which was not re-turned, Catherine was on her knees mopping up spilled milk while David practiced track runs in the hall. *Life* magazine had been torn limb from limb. The nurse's aide appeared in the doorway.

"We'd appreciate it," she spoke tersely, "if you'd stop letting him run up and down the corridor. Good gracious!" she paled, "you're not eating lunch in the dressing room!"

"Go back and tell your leader," Jim waved her away with a flourish, "We'd appreciate it if he'd give our son his X ray."

The aide turned on her heel and vanished through the center of the doorway. "Boy, what nuts! They're going to turn the place into a shambles."

"This is what I mean," Jim sipped his coffee and relaxed like a general in his encampment. The morale of the troops was at a high. "This is what I mean when I say we are better attuned to David's needs than they are, those so-called experts on children. The more David waits, the wilder he gets."

Catherine suppressed the temptation to ask Jim whether he didn't think David's excursions up and down the halls might not be a bit unfair, and that perhaps for the sake of the innocent they ought to restrain him. Hell, she gulped, this was war. He who was not with him was against him.

"You'd think they'd have some toys, something besides *Time*, *Life*, *Health* and *House and Garden*. Good thing," she winced at the rubbish on the rug, "we brought our own."

David had lain for a long time on the floor at Catherine's feet. Jim was dozing. Lollipop wrappers filled the ashtray. Catherine felt disheveled, her lap rumpled with the wet imprint of her son's behind. *House and Garden* had met the fate of *Life*. Jim had begun to grow a beard.

Suddenly, a new, dark-haired aide appeared at the dressing-room doorway, "Bring him along now, Mrs. Fitzgerald," she sang.

Jim and Catherine snapped to attention. They whisked David down to the X-ray room. A different young man in a white jacket hovered near them. The radiologist was a kindly, middle-aged nurse.

"The shifts have changed," Catherine whispered this intelligence to Jim, while he, smirking, carried David to the table.

"Place these protective shields between his head and your body. Better use your elbow, you may need both hands to hold his body." She turned to Jim. "Don't forget to use the shields when you hold his feet. Twist your body sideways away from his. He must be absolutely still or the picture won't come out."

The aide strapped David onto a long, black metal table. Above him there hovered the bird of prey, chrome and glass and steel, flanked with mirrors that uglified his fear. Jim thought of Abraham preparing his son to be the sacrificial lamb. The lamb bleated and struggled to get away.

"Get set," cried the nurse of the kind expression. "I'll count one, two, three, and he must be still."

The machine cranked abruptly into life and the bird of prey descended to its music. The aide pressed her elbow against the shield on the left side of David's head, Catherine following suit on the right. With one hand they held his trunk, with the other hand, his arm.

"One!"

Jim pulled his legs out straight and held them.

"Two . . . three!" was barely audible over the roar of the machine.

David looked like a deer in a wolf's embrace but he searched his mother's face and submitted.

✳

They recrossed the Bridge in the dark, sliding through its pale-lit web, its arches swinging to the stars. The glint of victory had already faded from their eyes. They thought of the work that lay before them. Patience, growth, love, these would be required, Jim reflected, to displace the accidental malice of a Nature that could maim. Not power, however purposefully deployed.

Before them lay the supreme test of their lives, he mused, the day-to-day struggle to endure. No, not just endure, Jim corrected himself, endurance is aimless and random. There must be life. Up onto the black road north they drove, forward to futurity, the night turning tired from the struggle but the day would begin again and begin again.

CHAPTER SIX

David hadn't noticed that his three older brothers were people. He never looked directly at them. If Mark, Danny, or Jonathan happened to be sprawled on the parlor rug, David might walk over one of their legs as if it were a bump in the carpet. And if one of them cried out in pain, he would respond with confused dismay as they might respond if their chairs howled suddenly. Sometimes he used their arms as if they were poles for reaching objects on the mantelpiece, seizing a limb, pulling and pointing it toward the thing desired until, at last, the arm acted as he wished.

Gradually, David began to change. He still snatched their favorite doodads, their Monster cards, or their rabbits' feet, but now he did it somewhat gingerly, as if he expected them to react. And react they did. More violently than the floor did when he fell on it or than the chair did when he ran into it. They were noisy, mobile, frighteningly unpredictable. But they were alive; that is to say, they did things which now awakened his interest.

One of their habits was to sit around on a rainy day in front of the coffee table in the parlor dramatizing battles on sketching paper. Mark might start the game with a drawing of the Civil War *Monitor*; Danny would add the *Merrimac*; and Jonathan, always inclined towards the exotic and the strange, would ink in, say, The Union Clam, a never-before-revealed secret weapon of Lincoln's navy that swallowed up fleets with a chomp. This joint drawing activity was always accompanied by oral explosions and rat-tat-tats, the artists rolling on the floor in glory or distress.

Catherine had been devoting a great deal of time lately to teaching David how to draw, making his hand trace objects, bringing him models from the garden. And David did produce: lines, circles, marks. But he did not seem satisfied; he no sooner set it down when he began at once to ink it out.

It was apparently the passion with which these sketching dramas were enacted that got to David. He began to like being nearby as they unfolded. Sidling into the parlor with his bag of blocks, he would watch their play through the corner of his eye. His own block creations grew more imaginative, as if by osmosis. And Danny, who had the best eye for that sort of thing, would often stop his own game and marvel aloud at David's bridges and towers.

David could make a train out of blocks. He could stick squarish pieces of paper on the wall and connect them, alas, with indelible ink. Why not draw a train? The idea suddenly forced itself on him one day when the three older boys were in the throes of drawing. He leaped up, ran to the table, wrenched a pencil from one of Jon's hands, and began making squares on their artwork. They reacted like an acting troupe interrupted in the midst of a performance by a drunk in search of the men's room. Though they sent up an awful howl, David knew that he could draw a train.

Train drawing became in fact David's main life plan for several weeks. He drew trains on the walls, trains on the floor, trains on the table, trains on the window, even on the glass. In fact he sometimes drew trains on his paper. In an effort to expand his artistic freedom, as Catherine put it, she bought him four quart jars of poster paint, a shock of pig-bristle brushes, an easel, and a smock. On the kitchen wall, he painted a train.

"Why don't you invite little Gar Baker over tomorrow?" Jim suggested as a train-drawing cure. "They had some of his paintings up on the wall when I went over to borrow the ladder yesterday. Really great for a four-year-old kid."

"As a matter of fact," Catherine rejoined, "I had Gar over this morning."

"Swell. Did you get out the paints?"

"Oh sure," Catherine answered noncommittally. "They had a pretty good time with them."

"Did they interact?" Jim corrected his educationese. "I mean how did the two of them get along?"

"OK," replied Catherine. "Except David isn't very good at sharing."

"So?"

"In fact he was so mad at Gar for using one of his brushes, he just up and painted Gar."

"Oh," Jim was disappointed but mildly amused. "Well, what

about procedure?" he inquired hopefully. "Did Gar show David how to paint on paper?"

"No," his wife answered. "And his mother wasn't too happy when I told her, but David showed Gar how to paint on walls."

"A leader," Jim proclaimed and they both began to laugh.

It was two weeks after the skull X ray and two weeks and a day after the electroencephalogram when Dr. Benjamin called.

"Well, my hunch was wrong," Dr. Benjamin cheerfully admitted. "He doesn't have arrested hydrocephalus. On the E.E.G., they got some paroxysmal abnormalities in the drowsy state, which confirms, in my opinion, that David has a number of gross signs of brain dysfunction . . ."

"The E.E.G. showed that, huh?" Catherine interrupted. She was trying to find a pencil with one hand and hold onto the phone with the other. Jim would want to know exactly what the neurologist said.

"It wasn't entirely conclusive. It usually isn't at such a tender age. But the electroencephalographer's comments plus the child's behavior in my office . . . And I hear his behavior at the skull X ray was so highly inappropriate . . ."

If inappropriate behavior was a sign of brain damage, Catherine reflected bitterly, then lots of luck to the staff of Children's Hospital.

"In fact," Dr. Benjamin went on, "The radiologist tells me it was almost impossible to X-ray the lad . . ."

"Oh, really?" Catherine permitted herself to think fiercely but she spoke in moderation.

"By the way, how's the little fellow getting on?" the confident voice interupted itself this time.

"Oh, fine. He's been drawing and painting. Trains mostly . . ."

"I mean behaviorwise. Are the drugs keeping him underwraps?"

"To tell the truth," Catherine answered. "I took him off the Dexedrine because he started acting like a clod."

"You've got to give these things time. It's important that David's behavior be controlled." Benjamin began to depart from his bedside manner. "You'll never get him into a nursery school if he acts as wild as he did when he was in my office."

I won't anyway, Catherine was thinking. Not until he's toilet-trained and they haven't developed a drug yet for that. She said,

"Don't you think his behavior will improve if he learns something?"

"I think his learning will improve if his behavior does."

"He can't learn anything if he's in a stupor all the time," Catherine's hackles rose ever so slightly. "Now, take his reading . . ."

"Mrs. Fitzgerald," Benjamin snorted, "I don't think that you are accepting the idea that your son is physically damaged. Let me emphasize, his problems are not educational, not psychological but physical. He may not be a mental defective but he is, nonetheless, grossly damaged . . ."

What did that mean in terms of David's present, his future, Catherine wondered. Did that mean that he would exist but never live; mark step but never grow? "What's the prognosis?" Catherine cut in. Her ears were turning red. She was fed up with explanations that explained nothing.

"I can't give you one now. Maybe in a year."

"Excuse me, Doctor, if I seem anxious, but please tell me what I should do, what I should expect."

"Give him the drugs," Benjamin melted a little. "Don't expect too much. Bring him back in six months to a year. We'll see if there isn't something then."

Catherine pictured herself throwing David into a closet until he was six months older. "But what about now?" she asked. "What are we going to do in the meantime?"

"Try to get him into a nursery school."

"But what if they won't take him because he's not . . .?" Catherine heard a click. The interview was over. She took out her journal on David's progress, and noted down just what the neurologist had said. She didn't really blame him. You can't go around asking doctors for advice and then not following it. Well, try again, she mused, taking down the bottle of pills, crushing one in a napkin with a hammer and mixing it with a glob of blackberry jam. David ate it while painting a purple train on the foyer wall.

✳

"Will anyone ever tell us what to do?"

"Benjamin can't because he doesn't know," said Jim, his cheeks bulging with meat loaf and potatoes. "Gosh, Catherine," he gulped, "go a little easier on the garlic."

"He ought to. He has tens of diplomas. He gets fat fees."

"But he's not responsible for the lack of research in the field. Look, if there was a brain-building pill, he'd give it to him. If there was an operation, David would get that. Besides you don't really want to take his advice. You don't want to give David the drugs."

"I would if they worked."

"Do you think you've really given it a decent try?" Jim looked directly at his wife.

"I don't know. What's a decent try? I gave him half a dose this afternoon."

"And?"

"You saw him when you came in. That's him by the window, The Man with the Hoe."

"And just when he was beginning to perk up," he conceded.

"I made the big mistake with Benjamin," Catherine confessed. "I mentioned the word 'reading.' You'd think I said 'bad breath' or 'socialized medicine,' he got so mad. I don't think he likes me."

"You're too sensitive. He told you before you're a good mother."

"Then how come he treats me like Medea?"

"Well, Catherine," Jim said slyly, "if you'd put a little humility into your mode of expression, I'm sure the good doctor . . ."

"I know I should have said 'word recognition,' not 'reading,' right? But I'm tired of playing games not to offend anybody. C'mon, Jim," she teased him back, "you won the philosophy medal in college. What shall we do about the drugs?"

"Depends," Jim kept up the game. "Are you an empiricist or an authoritarian?"

"That's easy," Catherine replied with a touch of bitterness, "an authoritarian. Trouble is the authorities won't accept my offer of prostrate submission. They make noises like my guess is as good as theirs."

"A sign of the times," sighed Jim.

"I wonder," he said, "if Benjamin thinks that David can't learn anything anyway, that we might as well forget it, and that the drugs'll at least make it easier on us."

"But he can learn."

"Of course he can. But can we teach him?"

The diagnosis of "brain-injured" that a second neurologist confirmed six months after David's visit to Dr. Benjamin did not help the Fitzgeralds penetrate David's private world or provide them

with visions of the future. While Catherine and Jim came to know
that their son's major deficit was not an innate failure of his intel-
lect but rather a crippling of his capacity to learn in certain ways,
there was no one to explain to them what effect the injury had
upon his powers to think and feel, what bounds it placed upon
ambition, or how they might be overcome. The professionals could
describe the "brain-injured" syndrome, a collection of traits all too
familiar, but no one was either able or inclined to tell which behavior poured from his cerebral wounds, which from a soul in mourn-
ing for its losses.

Was David's failure to speak derived from an assault upon his
brain, for example, or had the damage led him to avoid speech as he
avoided other contact with the world? Without some knowledge
of which brain functions might be affected, how these deficits
might in turn affect his capacity to learn, how they might be
shadowed forth by his mind's own night, there could be no plan of
attack upon David's problems, no strategy of healing, no life goals
wedded to reality.

Catherine and Jim were compelled to know their son as one is
compelled to know what one loves. They had to plumb the
mystery of his private world, discover what their two worlds had
in common, attempt to enlarge the common ground. They had to
discover and discover quickly before the closing of some secret
crypt that some small deed in the propitious hour might have left
ajar. They had to find out which, his frenetic searching or his
placid silence, impelled him more steadily toward the future,
whether their peace might not indeed be his despair.

There wasn't any deliberate plan developed on a particular day
in David's fourth year of life. They just began to observe their son
more and more closely, checking their observations with each
other, reconstructing his thought from their observations. Their
scrutiny was relentless.

And they discovered. They found, for example, that while
David learned, he did not learn very well through his ears. He was
not deaf. When the thunder clapped, he would look skyward.
When the telephone rang, he turned its way. When people spoke,
he came to watch their mouths. But it was rare when he understood what they were saying.

Everything his mother and father told him had to be told and
retold him again and again. "David, this is a *ball*, a *ball*. David, see,

a *ball*." Or, "See, David's running, *running* David." His memory of things he heard didn't seem to stick.

He did begin to talk but he talked in labels. He could report that a chair was a *chair* was a *chair*. But he didn't learn phrases of speech the way other children did. No "glass a'milk," no "gimme-dat." At night instead of rocking, he recited a litany of words but they were all nouns, all discordant, all concrete.

Catherine and Jim became convinced that somehow this inconsistency of hearing was at the crux of David's disability. They pursued it with the passion of parents trying to reach their child trapped in an abandoned well. Time was less critical, perhaps, but critical nonetheless.

"Even at that," Jim was telling Catherine, "he can't call up the words he wants when he wants to. Yesterday when I was taking him to the A&P, we passed this little brown dog on Brunt Street. Now you know he knows the word *dog* . . ."

Catherine nodded.

"God, he wanted to say it. He kept pointing at the thing. He kept whining, scrunching up his face, but he couldn't say it. Finally, when the dog was just about out of sight, he suddenly grabbed me around the head—I nearly lost control of the car—and he began to make my jaw move. When I said *dog* he seemed enormously relieved."

"He does that to me, too," Catherine was thinking aloud. "You know, there are some words he almost always remembers and always understands. Why those words and not the others?"

"True. He can take the plug out of the bathtub and put the drain back in if you tell him 'Take the plug out of the bathtub and put the drain back in.' And that's a pretty complicated direction."

Jim thought about the plug in the bathtub all the way to Marsdale the next morning. It was at the red light on the highway crossing that he discovered the answer and wished he could walkie-talkie Catherine.

"I got it. I got it," he tried telepathy. "He can remember the plug because he's done it. He's imitated us by pulling out the plug and putting in the drain. He associates . . ."

The car behind him was honking for Jim to go. He shifted into first and headed across the highway.

Let me think. Don't let me lose it, Jim struggled with his thoughts. He associates the word with an action he's performed.

When we say "pull out the plug," he pictures himself pulling out the plug. The action makes a memory so he remembers it.

Catherine was less concerned than Jim with whether words could be linked to kinesthetic memory. She worried about David's emotions. Even while Jim was enroute to Marsdale, she was racking her brain to remember the last time her son wept tears, when he last laughed aloud, how he showed a capacity to love. It was not his ability to perceive she wanted to scrutinize, but his ability to feel. That alone, she believed, would rescue him from emotional numbness—let him be what he ought to be.

And yet she wasn't sure. Jim had argued that the mind and soul are but aspects of the brain, the wounds of one the canker of the other. If they could discover what was wrong with David's brain and offer it some balm of learning, they might heal as well his spirit and his self.

"Doesn't everybody?" Catherine replied to Jim's announcement that David can remember words associated with actions he's performed even if he can't remember words associated with things he hears.

"Sure, but we don't need to," answered Jim abeam with victory. "You don't have to get a mental picture of an action every time you hear words. Maybe when you were a child and first learning you had to hear commands over in your mind or act them out mentally before you responded. But as you learned more and more language you could skip that step and just do what you were told. David never does get mental pictures of sounds. He couldn't think 'ding-ding' to save his life. But he can picture himself pulling out a plug."

Catherine closed her eyes and tried to think of David as a mechanism, an electric ear, perhaps, like the electric eye that opened a supermarket door. The electric ears responded only to certain sounds the way the eye responded to certain movements. It did not understand speech but if you said the words its machinery were wired to "hear," the door would open.

"Oh, God—it's so complicated," Catherine despaired. She put her head down on the table for a moment in the silence. Above them, ever-so-faintly where there was no rocking, she heard her son reciting his words the way another child might recite his prayers.

"The words," she cried suddenly. "Listen to the words!" Jim

looked as if she were foaming at the mouth. "The words he says in bed." Her eyes were on the ceiling. "Jim, they're all words David reads off cards!"

"Hey!" he came alive and caught the contagion of her find. In a twinkling Catherine had added a whole new dimension to their discussion. David didn't just have an action memory, he had a visual memory. "He's learning to hear through his eyes. And, in a sense, to speak through them, too."

It all made sense when you thought about it, Jim reflected next day on the way home. Somehow, that part of the brain which interprets and analyzes speech sounds had been damaged in David. It did not prevent him from hearing but it did prevent him from distinguishing sound units of the language. All sounds must seem to flow together. It would be like listening to Chinese. Not only wouldn't you be able to understand what was being said, he thought, you wouldn't even hear the separate sounds.

On the other hand, if the same noises were always associated with a certain action, like pulling out the plug and putting in the drain, you might even remember the noises too, at least enough to obey them. Even a dog understands English for "Do you want to go out?" And if the sounds were identified with written out words . . .

Catherine did not miss the significance of her find. It mattered that David could understand words through his eyes even if he could not perceive them through his ears. If he could read he could develop an inner life, running silent but deep within a full human person. Words are thoughts, feelings, hopes, desires. They can be lived even if they are not spoken.

That evening Catherine was tired. She had been through a thirty-minute tantrum with David, held off four more tests of will, completed three loads of laundry, tried to distract David's countless wanderings, drawer-rummagings, toy-box dumpings, and deal with three growing boys and a baby.

"Suppose your ears were of little use to you?" came from Jim through her weariness. "You heard things but they didn't seem to have much meaning. Follow?"

Catherine followed. Jim had made her see that David's pain and fears and dread yielded not to their abiding love alone but to the child's own sense of competence. Inwardness is not just given as a gift to a child, Catherine pondered, it is a meeting. Half-grace, it is also a struggle of the self out of the blood, and nerve and bone that are its bounds. Love waits, but can't the blood, and nerves and bones be also quickened?

"Uh-huh," Catherine answered stabbing a sock with a needle.

"You would have receptive or sensory aphasia," Jim reached down and pulled a slender book out of his briefcase, opened it to a place that contained a marker. "Meaning you would not be able to interpret the spoken language of others, to 'receive' what they are saying."

"I wouldn't be able to think a word and hear it in my head," rejoined Catherine. "Things I only heard I wouldn't remember."

"Cured!" Jim teased her. "Listen to this guy, Myklebust: 'It is not that these children cannot hear. They can hear but they have trouble in listening. This is the trouble they have in paying attention. To be able to listen means that you can pay attention to one sound, such as what the parents are saying, and not be disturbed by other sounds around you. This is especially difficult for the receptive aphasic.'"

"Sounds just like David, but exactly!"

"Not exactly," Jim corrected. "Earlier in this tome, it says the aphasic child cannot associate words with his experiences. But we two scientific observers have just discovered that he can. He has learned the words he sees on cards. He can even say them. And he can understand directions if he has carried them out before, to wit the plug and the drain. The only experiences he cannot associate with words are auditory experiences, right?"

"Right." Well, that was no small thing, their figuring out what might be wrong with David, Catherine mused.

"Which brings us to what we do about it. Say, don't stop teaching him to recognize words, I mean 'read,' will you?"

It stood to reason, Jim had mulled it over in his mind at the teachers' meeting that afternoon, that if David didn't have the ability to analyze speech sounds, he probably couldn't synthesize them either. How could he pull words out of a memory bank of speech sounds if no bank had ever been built up? You couldn't speak Chinese if you never really heard it. Ordinary four-year-olds no sooner had an idea when it was matched in their mind by a word, and automatically, without effort. David had to match his ideas with the written words on cards and then transfer that visual picture to speech somehow, and consciously, with enormous effort.

Thus, Jim concluded, he also had expressive aphasia, or trouble finding words. There would be things that they could do.

"Maybe we could tie him up and get him to learn to listen." Catherine made a stab at being facetious when she recalled that Jim had taught five classes that day, caught an early evening course at Newark, and must be tired too.

"The thing we've got to give this kid is a sense of success," Jim declared with unaccustomed potency and passion. "He's got to feel the world is worth living in, we've got to give him thoughts, cram his mind with meaning, tell him he does inherit the future."

"Amen," thought Catherine with a smile.

All human beings have an inordinate capacity to learn. And, as Catherine and Jim continued to discover, David was no exception. At first, the tasks they presented him with were aimed primarily at widening the area of communication between his mother and himself. Catherine bought him a puzzle with only three pieces and watched him cheerfully fit the pieces in. Then she made him sewing cards and watched his pleasure in lacing. His barrels and towers that fitted together were all self-correcting so he could not fail. Tasks that he could do well were always presented along with new problems so that he could first have success before he set forth to experiment. What gave him joy was not so much his contact with his mother, however, as his developing relationship to the world. External things were beginning to have meaning as if they were made for him and he for them.

In the weeks that followed their visit to Dr. Benjamin, Catherine and Jim felt David had made enormous strides. When Catherine cut pictures out of magazines and asked David "which is the lady" and "which is the vacuum cleaner," he could make the decision correctly. Since the words gave him so much gratification, she went on to teach him to recognize "eye," "ear," "mouth" as words that meant parts of his own body.

As June flowed into July, David began to look at the flowers in the garden and the birds in the sky as if the barrier of fright that had lain between him and them had vanished with the snows of winter and the pungent bedazzlement of spring. The mists in his eyes had lifted a little, blown by the breath of his inner life, quickened by his contact with the world.

David was more like other children. Yet he was not like them. He could climb stairs only lockstep like a toddler, closing the gap every time. Sometimes he put his head down to the plate and ate like a dog, voraciously without looking up. Sometimes he would not eat at all. He did not lose his pervasive sense of restlessness, his need to endlessly open cabinets and drawers, his requirement that every success be repeated *ad nauseam*. Under stress, he disintegrated into a flailing, screaming, lurching, wrenching creature. The slightest drop in temperature made him shiver with the cold. The slightest crack in a toy or the loss of a doodad made his whole body ripple into panic. He laughed in the wrong places at the wrong things. He did not seem to love. He had no tears with which to cry.

Catherine and Jim forgot his shortcomings, so great was their joy in his progress. But there were days when his mother feared he would always be apart, forever detached, never one with the mainstream of the world. So potent was his self-will at times, he seemed to see no power but himself. He needed to be more than a being, she concluded, defined by instincts and by things. He needed to be bound to the center of life in a way that he was not yet bound.

✳

What Jim and Catherine called David's progress was not evident to everyone. Or so they discovered that summer when they first came out of seclusion to entertain their friends.

It had been eight months since the couple had encouraged a social visit, and Catherine wanted it to be an occasion. Hers and Jim's day-by-day, week-by-week concern with David had made them, she confessed to her husband, obsessional bores. They needed a night of second-guessing the Government in Southeast Asia, of did-you-see-what-Lichtenstein-pulled-on-the-art-critics, or of just plain gossip. She had outdone herself by preparing pinwheel canapés instead of the usual crackers and cheese. She had shined the coffeepot and toaster in the kitchen, swept the tattered carpet in the parlor while the boys dusted every volume in the bookcase. The house glowed with a somewhat down-at-the-heels respectability. In the larder there was a choice of bourbon or Scotch.

Morris and Betty Benson arrived at 9:30, Ellen and Bill Murray soon afterward. The Levys came trailing in at ten, Sam telling at once his latest joke about the guy propositioning the girl at the party.

"I think I ought to warn you," the girl in the joke had cautioned, "I'm on my menstrual cycle."

"That's OK," Sam guffawed as he got it out, "I'll follow you on my Honda."

Morris and Bill traded a few more, and then Jim, who Catherine noted proudly was a brilliant conversationalist, turned the discussion onto the current fight over town zoning changes, drawing Bill and Morris into the kind of heat they loved. Well, if they don't, Catherine corrected herself, Jim does. Kate Levy was rooting for Morris and Sam was trying to tell another story. That left Catherine to engage Betty and El.

They both loved art, Catherine mused. She thought of asking them if they had seen Robinson's new show at the Graphic Associates when Betty began:

"How's David, Cath?" She turned her face toward El, who was sitting in the chair to Catherine's left. "You know David, don't you El? Isn't he just the most adorable, blond, blue-eyed heartbreaker you ever saw? Bet'll be the beau of Foster School!"

"He's doing so much better, thanks," she answered. "He paints; he's beginning to draw; he's doing puzzles; he's begun to like the boys."

"Down deep he's probably as bright as he is beautiful," Betty continued to effuse. She looked at El for confirmation.

"We're so glad for you," came El's slight flicker of a smile. "It's a shame about little Googie Marshall." She turned to Betty. "Did you know Jane finally had to put him in Warren State?"

Betty threw up her hands. Warren State was the local mental hospital.

"What was wrong with him?" Catherine asked.

"Poor little Googie," Betty answered. "He looked so awful. His tongue hung out and he drooled. Really out of it, mentally retarded."

"I heard he was brain-damaged," El spoke as if she knew. "And psychotic. They only put mentals in Warren State. They say the brain-injured do get psychotic at times."

"The Marshalls are such nice people," Betty bubbled. "It must have been simply awful. My sister had a mentally retarded boy," she shivered, "and they must have joined every self-help group in the Los Angeles telephone directory, but it didn't work. It was so hard on the other kids they had to put him away."

"The Marshalls waited too long if you ask me," El said with authority. "They're right down the street from me," she reminded Catherine, "and I can tell you that kid was a menace to the neighborhood. Besides being too much for Jane. Jane never had time for anything since Googie was born."

Betty was nodding in agreement.

"By the way, Cath," El asked pointedly, "you never do any of your felt collages any more, do you? Pity, they were so original."

"Did he attack other children?" Catherine was on the edge of her seat with curiosity, and ignored El's concern with what had been a hobby. There must be a reason why they found this Googie so repulsive.

"Well, not really," El confessed. "But you could never tell when he would. He was just like a wild animal. I nearly hit him once, he ran right out in front of my car."

"And he looked so awful," Betty put in with a wince of disgust. "He had these big gooey eyes, poor thing. Ssss," she shivered again. "And he made these animal noises. Jane had to change him till he was four or five. God, Cath, if you'd have seen him you'd realize how lucky you are David looks so good."

"How old is he?" Catherine asked, hoping that Betty and El did not know that David bleated like an animal, wasn't toilet-trained, wavered back and forth between their world and his own. She hoped there wasn't something they were trying to tell her. She wanted to remain as their friend.

"Five or six," El guessed. "If people would face up to the facts when these children are three or four, they might spare themselves . . ."

"Did he ever hurt anybody?" Catherine asked somewhat testily. She looked directly into El's blue crystal eyes glinting with righteous little flares.

"Cath, he was so awful," Betty answered for her. "He just couldn't . . . well, he just couldn't adjust to society."

Adjust to society? Catherine felt a twinge of pity, then of anger. Or was it that society could not adjust to him? They hate him, she thought with rising passion, they hate this five-year-old because he's ugly, different. Do they want me to hide David away in some asylum so they won't come to hate him too?

"Oh let's talk about something else," Betty moaned. She couldn't bear arguments, explosions, controversy or Catherine's troubled silence. "Googie," she nearly screamed her reassurance, "isn't one single thing like your David!"

But he was, Catherine mused. El knew he was. And though

Betty denied it, on some level she knew it, too. Inside him, David's sense of self flickered like Googie's between substance and shadow, trembled like an image in the water. It was only on the outside that her son's face, his stance, his shape proclaimed his normality, declared his sameness, demanded he be treated as a human child. Catherine knew these people—sensitive, compassionate, modern—could love the poison sumac in a sea of ferns, extol the odd-shaped fish on the ocean floor, reverence the freakish posturings of animals and birds because they live and life is good. It was only the strange in human form that must be feared, despised, concealed, hidden from the eyes that could not forgive it.

Catherine's face was flushed. Inside, she felt that she was bleeding. Should she plead with them, she wondered, should she not somehow make them understand? Should she tell them that David needed neither their denial nor concern, that they ought rather give him their respect? Was there not some way she might make them see that he had to fight to learn and learn to fight for all their children got for free? That he had more guts, more grit, more passion to overcome?

"Well he isn't normal, is he?" Catherine heard El's irked voice penetrate the mists of her musing. "It's no kindness," she instructed Betty sharply, "pretending to Cath that he's a person like anybody else, that he'll wake up one morning and not be a defective."

The evening took an eternity to end.

"You can't take to heart what everybody says," Jim said tiredly when the guests had left and Catherine reviewed the evening's altercation. "This is only the beginning. David will never have a bed of roses. Get used to it, Catherine, toughen up."

"Maybe I should've raised the roof?"

"What for? You can't teach people to love the stranger in one night's heat. Besides it's our opinion, yours and mine, that really matters at this stage of the game. Be sure of your own feelings, that's all." Jim yawned and stretched out on the couch.

Catherine nodded. How like them, she smarted still, how like life that while some are working tirelessly, earnestly for a miracle, there are others who don't especially care if it happens. El, she charged, she might have seen that child's despair, listening, heard his cry. Was he not forsaken because he was forsaken?

Jim fell to dozing on the couch but Catherine could find no peace within herself. She tried to imagine their son as she had lately seen him. At first, he appeared in front of the form board whipping in the forms in forty seconds, smiling, normal, his mother marveling at the clock.

But that tableau quite suddenly dissolved. Now he stood at the window, shallow and unfeeling his eyes gazing dumbly into space. Now he turned for no clear reason, biting, drawing blood from his frantic hand, his eyes as glassy as poor Googie's, his solid head smashing on the floor. Which was David? Catherine's mind was screaming now with panic. Who, what creature, was their son? Jim flopped over on the sofa as if her silent tremulo were heard.

Could he not be both, normal, abnormal, either, all, Catherine asked herself. His life existed not in names or signs, she saw at last, but in reality. His humanity was the possible dream uncurling in his life unto its limits; not a label, not an arbitrary standard, not some confusion of the real things of this world with terrible pictures. He was what he was; the joy of him was in what he must be, not fully born perhaps as no man ever is, but real. That which is real ought always have its life.

Catherine rose, opened the door to the darkness, searched the stars for evidence of God. "Forgive me," she said. "Forgive me, David, for not seeing. Forgive me for believing with them that normal and abnormal really matter, that less than normal is somehow less than human. You are my son," she sobbed, "and perhaps one day a person in full dimensions." She prayed for a sign that that day would come. And the starlight poured its mystery on the grass.

✳

The nursery-school lady had eyes like burning marbles that could coldly compel or melt to liquid when she laughed. She made David look at them whenever she spoke though he twisted his neck and wrenched his body, not wanting to care what she wanted.

The others took off their coats and hung them up. They took down the paints, got out the paper, painted their pictures, and put the paints back. But David did not wish to do what the others did. Not at first. He would have his own purposes, his own purposelessness, scorning playmates, ignoring helpmates, playing out his own dreams for his own sake only.

The school lady had a way of crashing in. She could make his hands undo his coat and his legs propel his body to the hook, and his whole self reach for the hanging. Her strength made him stretch for the orange-juice cans full of colors. And the colors no longer blinded and frightened since he had learned their names at last and thus found the secret of their power.

"David," she would call and he would come, not just because he knew and valued the sound of his name, but because the school lady met him with the sweet aroma of sandtarts that he had helped her bake, and the odor of raw wood that he had helped her saw, and the faint smell of painted macaronis he had helped her string.

The others did not interest him, not at first. He was the bridge he built of blocks when he felt like bending, the train he painted when he felt like rolling. He was cold when he went out without his coat, and black and yellow and purple and green when he splashed the paint upon the paper. And his heart leaped at Fred, the big, black dog.

The wind had a whistle. The sun cooked him brown around the edges like a sandtart. And when the school lady made him balance on a swing, his head tingled to the roots of his hair, and his heart fell through a hole in his stomach. Birds ate peanut butter off the pine cone his mother let him hang upon the tree. His legs made the tricycle go. He teased a turtle with a twig and studied the guppies in the bowl. He heard thunder, and was tickled by the rain.

The others made words at him but he didn't answer. Then one day they made stories for the school lady and her mouth smiled and her eyes melted like brown butter. David wanted to make a story too but he could not think the words, and his legs kept driving him aimlessly in circles. She was still listening, still laughing, still putting her arm around the others. If only she would wait, wait until the words came, wait until his feet would stop their moving. He fell upon the floor, put his hand on the yellow truck and walked it on his knees across the floor. "Truck," he thought, the word from the card popping into mind. "Trucks . . . ," he seized the school lady's head and made her look. "Trucks" with all his strength he cried, "Trucks . . . go!"

✳

From the very beginning of her own consciousness, Maggie had fancied David even though he had the habit of turning into a robot whenever she was carried into the room. She liked him because he was small compared to the other people in the house. And such was her infantile egocentricity, she did not detect that her affection was not returned.

A more passive, less demanding, less volatile infant might have been passed over in those exacting days of David's crisis. But, as Jim cooed at her when he held her on his lap, "You're a chip off the old Earth Mother, Maggie, the second hardest gal in the world to ignore."

Just as when an infant, Maggie had insisted on being held, fed, played with, entertained no matter what tragedy was being enacted, so as a toddler she demanded David's court. After all, the older boys had given her to understand she was the most marvelous, funny, desirable, outrageous person in the world. Why had David failed to pay her homage? Clearly, she would have to intervene.

Jonathan had taught Maggie at eight months to hurl Wheat Chex at distant targets while seated in her jump seat after breakfast. It was part of the boys' long-range goal to make Maggie the best pitcher in the T-Shirt League when she finally would reach the age of reason. When David would suddenly turn off his feelings as Maggie entered the room, she would wait until her bowl was filled then lob the bits of cereal at his face. The effect was to startle him to attention.

Later, when David learned to draw on paper on the floor, Maggie would crawl over and sit on his half-made sketch. Unless David recognized her presence, he could clearly do nothing in his own defense. She would just sit there, her saucy, upturned face defying him to make her go away. At first, David regarded his sister as a natural disaster, as if she were a stone that had rolled unwittingly on his drawing, unwanted but impossible to move.

Then, one day, this outrageous stone, not content with sitting on his drawing, tore it up and placed it in its mouth. The effect was instantaneous. Rising in a wrath, David yanked the sketch away from his sister, bleating, disappeared into the parlor, a wailing toddler in pursuit.

Maggie staggered towards him, David falling from couch to chair, desperately trying to get away, she screaming, he yelping. Then suddenly he stopped. He looked at this howling misery anew. She was the impotent one, the frustrated one. It was he who had the power, was out of reach. He giggled. He let her pull his hair and he laughed some more. Then she laughed. "Ma, Ma," she chirped. "Ma, Ma." The sound set him frowning in disgust. "Mommy," David corrected. And with an air of cavalier contempt for those who can't even speak the language, he rose, turned on his heel and strode away.

*

"It's hard on him knowing that he's different from the other children, but I don't think he'll let it break him." Catherine was thinking over what Mrs. Patman, the nursery-school teacher, had said. She wondered when David began to know, or, indeed, if he did know.

Of course, Catherine trusted Mrs. Patman's judgment implicitly. Not that Mrs. P. had any degrees or status in the field of special education. Not that David loved her with the take-care-of-me attachment he directed toward Mary, her able assistant. Not that Mrs. Patman acted as if she ever accomplished anything important in her long life. She was thin, gray, wrinkled, growing old. She stuttered and she did not pretend to be wise.

Mrs. Patman was wise, however. She was observant, creative, compassionate, idealistic. And she knew what to do. "Thank God," thought Catherine as she sat in her kitchen over Saturday morning coffee waiting for little Gar Baker to arrive. "Somebody knows what to do."

Mrs. Patman believed in life, Catherine mused. Not that she ever said she did. She just lived like she did. Hers was a nursery school for normal children, Catherine supposed, a great Victorian house with its dark eaves and ancient oaks, an anomaly in suburbia. All kinds of children came, however. Once, a blind child whom the other children helped to ride a tricycle by crying out "red" when she rode toward an obstruction, and "green" when the way lay open ahead. Once, a deaf child, another time, a mongoloid, another, a schizophrenic. They all grew, all thrived; some she saw graduate from public school; all were recipients of her nagging, driving, believing gift of grace, her investment in their development more than their comfort and affection, her insistence that they live life fully.

Mrs. Patman had taken David, toilet-trained or not, and then proceeded to train him. She and Mary forced him to fit into the structure of the school, the day-to-day routine of passing out cookies, wearing a napkin on his lap, putting back the tools when he was finished. They taught him to defy his fears by riding high on the swing, climbing the monkey bars, crawling across the six-foot horizontal ladder and swinging down. They introduced him to finger painting, clay modeling, cutting, sawing, hammering, all forms of self-expression which helped him compensate for his loss of speech. But Mrs. Patman wondered what special prod he needed to "warm to the other little children."

Jim, who had just finished shaving, skipped out of the downstairs bathroom looking fresh as the proverbial daisy. "Why so pensive?" he demanded of Catherine, just crushing out her cigarette in the ashtray.

"I was just trying to think about activities for Gar and David. Today's David's day for relating to other children. Then I started thinking about the Patman School and Mrs. Patman . . ."

"So was I, come to think of it. I decided there's only one thing the Patman School lacks, and do you know what that is?"

Catherine shrugged. Jim was in one of those silly, joyous moods of his and Catherine didn't know what was coming.

"A fight song!" Jim said enthusiastically. "Behold the debut of the 'Patman Fight Song,' written and composed while shaving by none other than James T. Fitzgerald, songster."

Jim struck up a pose like a college cheerleader. He sang:

> We climb the monkey bars for Patman,
> We're winners at free pla-aaay.
> As for social interaction
> It's Patman all the way. Hey, hey, hey.

Catherine buckled up with laughter. Jim went dancing toward the parlor to rouse the older children to the fight song.

There was a faint knock at the door. Catherine hollered over the uproar, "Get it, Jim, will you? It must be Gar!"

Gar stepped confidently into the kitchen bearing a box of something, mostly crayons, chirruping, "How d'y do Mrs. Fitzgerald?" Jon was relieving him of his possessions, Danny offering him a cookie. Only David regarded him with apprehension. He fled into the bathroom by the kitchen.

"Come on out, David," Catherine called. "Don't be an old stick-in-the-mud. Gar wants to play with you."

Jim hadn't been paying much attention when David brushed past him and ran upstairs. Then the scene finally struck. "You don't think he's hiding from Gar, do you?"

Within moments, Catherine and Jim were pleading, calling, coaxing David to come down and play with Gar and trying to keep Gar from deciding to go home. They offered him candy, puzzles, piggyback rides, but none availed.

"Mrs. Patman says he knows he's different. Do you think he knows?"

"Of course he knows," Jim answered without hesitation. He strode into the kitchen as if he had an idea in mind. "But being different isn't always bad."

Reaching for the stack of cards on top of the refrigerator, Jim pitched his voice ceilingward. "C'mon down, David," he called. "Show Gar how you can read your words."

In three seconds, David emerged at the bottom of the stairwell, his face glowing with a smile. "Sidewalk," he shouted from twenty feet away. "Kitchen," he read across the kitchen.

Mark, Danny, and Jonathan had begun cheering by now, Baby Maggie joining in.

"Oooo, he can read," cried Gar.

He and David painted together.

CHAPTER SEVEN

Seascape on the Jersey shore was not even remotely pretentious. Its houses built in the early twentieth century paled before the haloed haze of August, bleached Victorian, small town American. The sand was cornmeal. The sea had conservative vitality. The winds sang safety, drowsiness, and peace.

The Fitzgeralds had decided to treat themselves to their first vacation in five years, choosing Seascape for its family-centered pace, its tolerance for children, the slap of its gentle surf. David would be five years old next month and enrolled in the County's special class for brain-injured children. For his sake, Catherine and Jim hoped the two weeks at the seashore would help him overcome his deep attachment to Sarah, his counselor for six weeks at a special day camp in southern New York. For every waking hour he called her name. He even learned to write it in the sand.

David took to the ocean at once, racing the sandpipers across the dunes, black-headed gulls swooping, Jonathan crying he just saw a whale. He joined his brothers on a search for seashells, lugging home a bag of fan-shaped clams. He watched the minnows whiz like darts, picked up a crab at dusk on the darkening shore. He plunged, leaped, rolled like a porpoise in the sea, felt the sad, sighing labor of the surf, sighing "Sarah."

Saturday, Sunday, Monday, there was sun. Sun for swimming, sky for kiting, bright morning for searching for the osprey whose nest hung like a hairy raft on the telephone lines; sun for baking in, sun for crabbing in, sun for dulling the memory of Sarah.

Then Tuesday, it rained. The sea was a cold, green silk, iced with lace. The air seemed spun from night and water, a gold strand of sun sliding through. David lay on the floor of the cottage moaning at the fog as it wept on the windows. He mentioned Sarah.

"Well, he's got good taste, anyway," Jim said of Sarah, recalling her youthful confidence, the curl of her chestnut hair, the peach glow of life on her cheek. "Don't blame him a bit."

"Mark," Catherine commanded, "write out 'Sarah' for him on the pad, will you? It seems to pacify him."

Mark groaned something about being in the middle of *Kidnapped*, but he printed S-A-R-A-H in large letters on David's scribble pad. "We ought'a get five big gold and red SARAH banners and hike 'em up on top of the house or something," Mark said peevishly.

"Yeah," agreed Danny, who was somewhat jaundiced towards females.

"Wish he hadn't got so attached," Catherine mumbled behind the novel she was reading. Would he ever get over it, she wondered.

The weather made Catherine feel tight and hard. She drew into herself to avoid the gloom of the elements. Sound, the touch of light vexed her skin. The dampness was assaultive.

All the boys were reading. David traced his favorite name on the pad. Maggie, newly roused from her nap, went around beating each low head with a sticky lollipop, thus assuring herself some attention.

"You were the one who used to worry about his shallow feelings." Catherine was surprised to hear Jim answer.

She pulled herself wearily up from the wicker chair and went to find a diaper for Maggie. Through the window she saw the steel-gray sea, the sand like ashes on the shore.

On-the-Edge, which sounded more like a state of mind than a day camp, was operated for brain-injured and emotionally disturbed children six miles south of the Fitzgeralds' home at Warren. Catherine and Jim, ordinarily not affluent enough to send their children to camp, had managed to scrape together the four hundred dollars required to provide David with a "structured situation" for six weeks that summer. Moreover, Catherine had needed a car in good working order to transport him the twelve miles daily. And then there was the vacation for the rest of the family.

Catherine had tried not to worry about the money. She thought instead how it was all worth it, worth it because of Sarah. The nineteen-year-old had had three children in her charge, but it was David she adored. Mrs. Patman had made David draw from himself, Catherine reflected, but David drew from Sarah. Children need both kinds of love.

"It's amazing how David's changed our values," Jim interrupted Catherine's thoughts. "There wasn't any question what we needed most this summer, a new couch and a rug or David to go to On-the-Edge."

"On-the-Edge," Catherine laughed every time she heard the name. "That just about sums up my attitude in June when nursery school ended."

They sat down together while Catherine made the salad for supper, congratulating each other on the year's successes. Danny's "near-blindness," attested to by a bona fide ophthalmologist, had disappeared once he was promoted out of Mrs. Fellini's class. Jim had got a raise. Mark, Danny and Jonathan had won the fifth, third, and second grade poster contests respectively. Dr. Benjamin thought David "much improved."

"Of course the house hasn't been painted in eight years. There's a two-foot-square hole in the living room rug. The upholstery's pouring out of the couch. And the tiles in the bathroom have come up."

"Everybody thinks we're eccentric . . ." Catherine put in.

"And David's in love."

David still lay on the floor, but now he had one foot cocked up playing with the cover on the wicker couch. He was smiling. In his mind, he was teasing Sarah, who wanted him to get up and put on his swimming trunks. He saw her scolding him, then coaxing him, now tickling him. She couldn't be irked with him for long.

"Still," Catherine groaned, "I just wish he hadn't got so attached. Why couldn't Sarah have treated him the way Mrs. Patman did?"

"Aha, the green-eyed monster," Jim said, slyly hinting that David's mother was a bit jealous of David's first love. "You know I think Mrs. Patman sort of set up David for Sarah. She helped him be aware of himself. Made him develop his consciousness of other people."

"He didn't always like it but she was good for him," Catherine said firmly.

"Well, she intruded into his life, but to make him develop his sense of being . . . of being a person."

"As we did . . ."

"Yes, we did, too. But parents are always there, taken for

granted. We're the constant stars, or at least we should be. We're human objects, servicers of needs. As time goes on, we flesh out, take on dimensions . . ."

"But he has never really focused on us as people," Catherine sounded sad.

"Children never see their parents as people, I hear, until they're parents themselves."

"And he never saw Mrs. Patman as a person either?"

"Probably more as a guiding force, the Teacher." Jim watched a fly light on the half-cut Jersey tomatoes that somehow made him think of cherries and Old Fashioneds. "How 'bout a drink?" he asked.

After lunch they went out walking. A curtain of fog had fallen on the shore, hiding the ocean from eyes not twenty yards away. Through the mists, people moved like spirits, coming into view, Catherine thought, as merest shadows. And they passed, still shadows, never assuming in that fog their human form though they nearly touched, heard the other's voice, or waved familiarly. Is that what people are to him, Catherine asked herself. Beyond them as they walked emerged the ocean's silhouette beating like a brooding heart against the ghostly shore.

No, Catherine answered herself, it is not David who adds up the He and the He and the He into the It. It is we. David has not learned to abstract that well, to suppress as we do life into its elements, to harden men into things among things. Whatever issues out of the fog into his life, he meets. The sea gull, more than as a picture, a splash of black and white against the gray sky; more than as its movement, an image gliding towards the trembling sea; more than by its laws, its species, its numerical relation, he encounters the bird itself, whole and single and exclusive.

Perhaps this is the mystery of David, Catherine thought, the mystery of his love for Sarah. Perhaps he has the rising power, the sense of a self no longer emptied of reality, the freshness of one who is newly born. For he has no words, no precepts, no directions to make him grasp Sarah as an object, compare her with other objects, establish her in her order among the classes. She did not enter the structure of his knowledge, a thing among things, an event among events. She was as he found her, and is, from the comb in her pocket to the radiance of the world in her eye, present and unique. All things live in the light of her, and in the light of

the sea gull, and in the light of all he encounters without conditions, as if he were made for them and they for him.

Jim had gone off with Maggie in his hand groping in the fog for
David chasing a one-legged sandpiper. Catherine wandered alone
on the shore listening to the moaning of the surf.

How I worried about the depths of his feeling, his power to be
human, Catherine mused, as if social effectiveness were the sole
way to share in life. We need skills and knowledge to do our work,
but we need the will to embrace life whole in order to be human.
Sometimes the search for knowledge and social power separates us
from reality and lets us be overwhelmed by things. Less differenti-
ated, less an individual, perhaps our son was also less estranged.
Perhaps he has been tied to the center of life in a way we could not
fathom.

Two days later, the sun shone again at last, an explosion of light
bluing the ocean, whitening the shore. Before it moved westward,
it poised far out over the Atlantic to drop its spangles on the sea.
Catherine and Jim, Mark and Danny caught three crabs before
they buried themselves in the slope between the sandbar and the
shore. David flew a kite his grandmother had sent for to a canned
pea company, two labels and a dime. That evening the family
trooped off to the amusements in town, the go-cart rides and the
trampoline.

Everybody wanted to try the trampoline but only David had
experience. Sarah had taught him to leap high at the day camp, and
leaping well had become a matter of pride. He removed his shoes in
front of the wide pit across which stretched the tensile canvas.
Then he stepped in place, smiled and let his body reach. Up, up, up
he sailed as if he had made a compact with the air, plummeting,
touching, flying up again, filling the heavens, soaring out beyond
the world.

Three trampolinists who had been demonstrating their athletic
prowess to each other stopped and watched and smiled at David
leaping, his family screaming with delight. It was not his gymnas-
tics that intrigued them. They were simple enough. Nor was it his
triumph in the arena's glaring lights. They caught the joy in his
truly speaking glance, the flight of his spirit with his body, his soul
unbound. "Sarah," he said as he came to rest, "Sarah."

"Sure, he'll get over it," Jim told Catherine as they were packing up for the homeward trek, knowing he was whistling in the dark.

"How?" his wife nearly screamed. "If he hasn't gotten over it with all these distractions, what'll he do when he gets home?"

"He's happy, Catherine." Jim reassured. "He's happier than I've ever seen him. In that sense, I hope he never gets over it." Jim slowly piled his shirts into the metal trunk that would fit into the back of the car.

"But he'll suffer," Catherine moaned. "He'll be so down when he discovers she's gone forever."

"I wonder," said Jim. "I doubt that we ever forsake our Sarahs."

School began on a Friday in September. David hoped Sarah would be there. He let his mother and father dress him in his new clothes, slick down his hair with perfumed lanolin, insist he eat an egg as well as cereal.

"Now, Jim," Catherine explained, "he might not eat his lunch in some strange place."

David winced before the orange-and-black school station wagon with only momentary shyness. He looked bravely at the other boys. He carried his lunch box in his gym bag, let his seat belt be fastened, let the other boy lean heavily on his arm. He did not wonder why his father talked so much or why his mother began to cry.

He liked having his own desk. The room was nice. But Sarah wasn't there. A lady was there who kept making him listen the way Mrs. Patman did. There was his need to move, to touch, to open things, to run, to hide within himself. The panic was there. But Sarah wasn't.

"Sarah's all gone." Catherine tried to put the situation in terms David could understand that evening before he went to bed. She foresaw a miserable weekend now that David knew Sarah would not be at the school. She wondered whether David would want to return on Monday.

David looked up at Jim as his father tucked him in bed.

"Sarah's all gone," Jim said quietly.

David turned away, pulling the covers up over his head.

"Does he understand?" Catherine wondered aloud as they sat reading the evening paper together.

"He understands here," Jim answered pointing to his head, "but not in here," he gestured toward his heart. "I don't know whether he's capable of grieving in the way we think of it," Jim sighed. "But maybe he has to grieve before he can yield Sarah up to the past."

"He missed me when I went to the hospital that time for the operation. Remember? When he was fifteen months old?"

"Oh, I remember all right," Jim groaned. He put his hand on his chin in the reflex of meditation. "But it wasn't integrated. I mean he didn't feel sorrow in a way that had meaning for him. He was just lost, forsaken. He didn't smile; he didn't even strike out. He just sat there. Infants grieve that way, they say. They just decline and keep declining until their mothers return."

"God, you don't think he'll do that?"

"Catherine, he's not declining. Children and adults overcome their sorrow by expressing grief directly, often by weeping and moaning. It gives their loss meaning . . ."

"That lets him out," Catherine said sadly. "He can't cry tears. He hasn't wept in over a year. Oh, Jim, it might have been better . . ."

Better if he had not met Sarah? Jim thought not. Sarah gave him joy. Would it be amiss if she also taught him sorrow? Who has lived who has not been touched by life's extremes? Who has felt existence without ecstasy and sorrow? Who has not been warmed by the image they left behind?

On Saturday morning, Catherine and Jim were awakened by David's restless bleating. Mark had given him his cereal. Danny had amused him with his plane. Nothing seemed to please him. "Sarah?" he kept asking, "Sarah? Sarah?"

"Sarah's gone away." Jim stumbled sleepily out of the bedroom, hitching up his pants. "Sarah will not be at David's new school because Sarah had to go away."

"Sarah," David repeated this time without the question. He wandered into the parlor to find his box of letters. Catherine had shown him how to spell some words.

"Yay," David applauded himself for finding his alphabet. "Yay" was what the boys always hollered when David grandstanded with his words. "Yay" to David meant cheering David up. Only now David seemed to be doing the cheering. His parents found him alone, clapping his hands.

Then, a few seconds later, as Catherine had put on the coffee and was about to fry Jim an egg, David reappeared in the kitchen. He ran straight to the downstairs bathroom.

Jim followed, quietly opening the bathroom door right after David had closed it. Inside was his son, dabbing his eyes with toilet paper, wet with water from the bowl.

"Jim, he's acting crazy. I think. We're going to have to see to it that he never . . ."

"Shhh," Jim hushed her.

Through the open bathroom door they could see that David had placed the toilet seat at which he usually urinated up against his face. The lid made an angle against his eyes. He seemed to be squeezing them until they hurt. Was he trying to cry, Jim wondered.

"Sarah?" he asked.

"What's he . . . ?" started Catherine. Jim hushed her again.

David had left the bathroom for the wooden puzzle in the bedroom. "Yay," he echoed when he found the proper piece.

"Come here, David," Jim called with a confident note in his voice. "Come here, son, Daddy wants to help."

Jim led David into the kitchen, sat him down on a kitchen chair, then went over to the kitchen sink. He took a soft washcloth, soaked it in water from the spigot, and brought it over to his son. David grimaced like a child on the verge of sorrow. Jim dabbed each eye with the dripping cloth.

Great watery "tears" went streaming down David's face, riding the ridge of his chin onto his shirt. "Sarah," David moaned out of his streaming cheeks as if the stone of his sorrow had come soft. "Sarah all gone." His face darkened into wretchedness. Here was grief where it had never been before. "Bye Sarah."

Then he slipped from the kitchen chair as if a great load were lifted from his soul. The "tears" dried, he pushed a car along the floor. "All gone, Sarah," he said with a touch of wisdom. "All gone."

Catherine, who had filled up herself, looked at Jim, whose face glowed with quiet triumph. "Blessed are they who mourn," he said, "for they shall be comforted."

As will those who struggle, and those who live.

THE CHIRPING OF A SPARROW
By Carol Panter

CHAPTER ONE

It was an ordinary day in November. A weak, chilling rain had started to fall at about noon, cancelling our last hockey game. It was the day that Princess Elizabeth was marrying Prince Philip. The school bus let me off in front of our apartment building. In two years, when I will be in Third Form, I'll be old enough to take the subway. I was thirsty.

Willie, the old Scotchman who operated the elevator on our side of the building, could always provide an accurate account of what to expect in any particular apartment. He offered the information without the slightest solicitation. But one came to depend on it. For example, Willie might say, "Just took your mother, your granny, and another lady up, Janie. They'll be having a cup o' tea, I'd guess." That would be my signal to straighten my falling hair before the gilt-edged mirror of the rising elevator, tucking my collar back into my coat. Nothing like walking in on a tea party.

Or Willie would say, "It's just your sister up there today, Janie. She beat you in by fifteen minutes, easy."

"It's no race, Willie," I would reply. "The Lower School gets out earlier."

Sometimes, on a Saturday when my mother was giving a women's luncheon, my father used Willie as a lookout.

"They're still up there, Mr. Goldstein," Willie would warn, pulling open the heavy door to the elevator. "Still goin' full blast." My father would thank him for the report and then head right back to his club for an additional hour of steam or squash, or whatever it was that he did on a Saturday afternoon when there was no golf.

Today Willie told me that the doctor was in my apartment.

"Which doctor, Willie?"

"You know, princess, the one they call for the kids."

"Dr. Green?"

"Yes, that's the one."

Willie was silent, allowing me to digest the news. Perhaps he hoped for an explanation. Often he reported the fact that Dr. Green was paying a call even if it had nothing to do with me at all. Just yesterday he said, "Chicken pox up there in 14C. All three kids down with 'em. Doc's been here two times today . . . Just took him down no more than five minutes ago."

Or occasionally, in the case of true excitement in the building, he might tell of an incident from another wing.

"Lotta action here today, Janie. Over at Penthouse West. One o' those psychiatrist ladies. Gets a guy in her office, a kid he was really, an' the next thing you know, he's out there on the terrace ready to jump. We had two fire trucks, nets an' all, and three cop cars. Got here no more 'an one minute after the call went out. Like they was waiting around the corner. You shoulda seen it, Janie."

His eyes gleamed brightly as he brought the elevator to the landing. Fifteenth floor. But he made no attempt to open either the elevator's gate or the heavy door which led to a long, narrow vestibule. This was where the people waited for Willie to pick them up when they came out of their apartments. There was one on every floor.

Sometimes we would stand there talking until we were interrupted by the elevator's buzzer signaling insistently that someone on another floor needed to go up or down. Today would have been one of those quiet days, a rainy afternoon, not many calls for Willie, some local gossip to discuss; it was just right.

Except that Dr. Green was in my apartment. That was disturbing. Willie had noticed too. Dr. Green is our pediatrician. But there were no children home now.

And then I had this terrific desire to get to our refrigerator and drink something cold. As if it were July, not November. And I'd just had a drink right before I left school.

"What happened, Willie? To the man on the roof? Did he jump?"

"Naw," said Willie with open disappointment. "The doc got out there and started talkin' to the lad, tellin' him that he'd be takin' the wrong way out and all their sweet-talk. Before you know it, my dearie, down he come from the ledge on his own, tame as a newborn lamb. Then the firemen stopped jiggling their nets and the policemen went off on their business and soon you'd never know there'd been anything out of the ordinary goin' on around here. So there you are. Your mother'd have had a ringside seat if she'd been home lookin' out the winder."

Perhaps he sensed that today I could not stay longer. He opened the elevator gate and then the heavier outer door and I turned toward my apartment. There was only one other on our floor. A table stood in the center of the vestibule, a Dansk basket filled with dried flowers in the middle. My mother and Mrs. Fox, our neighbor, took turns replacing the flowers whenever a drunk party guest ruined the arrangement by choosing a dried cocoa flower for a lapel or some other mysterious use. The flowers were rigid, odorless, and in my opinion, only one step above being a bucket of dead weeds.

" 'Bye, Willie. Take it easy, now." It was what I always said to Willie.

" 'Bye, Janie. You're a nice girl," Willie replied. It was what he always said to me.

Before I could get my key out, the front door flew open. There was my mother, looking oddly disheveled. She wore no makeup, none of her usual jewelry, and there were certain sections of her hairdo that were pointed in the wrong direction. My mother would not usually open the front door in this condition. Even for me. My father often teased that if there were a fire, Mother would surely be consumed in the flames as she coaxed the last hair into place. I wondered if it had something to do with the boy on the psychiatrist's terrace. Even though this didn't seem like the proper connection, there was no ignoring that *something* was amiss.

If Mother looked distraught, she acted worse.

"The bus," she said as I walked in, "it's never been as late as this. What happened? Did you stop off somewhere?"

"No." Usually she kissed me. Not that I like it. But today she didn't try.

"I've . . . we've been waiting for you, Jane. Dr. Green is here. He's in the library." Her voice had softened.

"Dr. Green is waiting for *me*?" I asked. It was the first time that I felt a foreboding flash: the trouble had something to do with me. Busy Dr. Green sitting around waiting for eleven-year-old Jane Goldstein to come home from school. It just didn't add up. And my mother, looking kind of dazed, like a sleepwalker almost, saying words, but acting as if she needed someone to take her by the hand and show her what to do. Something crazy was happening, all right.

"OK, I'll be right in. I just want to put some of this stuff away." I needed a drink. My mother seemed relieved that I was not about to question her further.

"Don't be long," she said and started toward the library. I went directly to the kitchen without removing my coat. Swinging the refrigerator door open wide, I quickly searched the shelves. Something cold. Something wet. There. A half-bottle of ginger ale. I threw my head back and tilted the bottle upwards. The half-flat liquid felt shocking against the back of my throat. It was as cold as I had hoped. In an instant, the bottle was empty. My thirst, which had been momentarily quenched, was again raging. My lips were dry, my mouth parched. I needed more.

There was a quart of orange juice from breakfast. I put it to my lips. The relief of the cold juice against my acrid throat was frightening. I would be consumed. I gasped for breath. I was taking such enormous swallows that I was simply opening my throat and pouring the liquid down.

More. A can of tomato juice. Most of a quart of milk. Cold and wet. It had only to be cold and wet. Any flavor, texture, color. Fruit, vegetable, dairy product; they were indistinguishable. The only requirement was that it be cold and wet.

What had detained me? I knew that they would soon be investigating. As I was leaving the kitchen, I passed the sink. A tumbler stood on the drainboard. Quickly picking it up, I opened the faucet, filled the glass and consumed its contents in almost one motion. By the time I had walked the few steps down the hall to where my mother and Dr. Green waited, I was again as thirsty as if I hadn't had a drink in a week.

✳

"Dr. Green would like to have a specimen of your urine."

"My ur . . .? But you just got one last . . ."

"I know, Janie. Last week."

Dr. Green looked uncomfortable. His collar seemed to be cutting his neck. He said, "There's something that we're not sure about, Jane. That's why I would like to repeat the test. Just to make sure. We wouldn't want even the littlest doubt, would we?"

Dr. Green. Took care of almost every kid I knew. I can't even remember when he wasn't my doctor. He'd give me the different shots before summer camp, the ones which made my arm blow up like an angry balloon. Once in a while, my sister or I would get really sick with a high fever and chills and our mother would call him out at night. Then she'd rush around, straightening the room out so that he wouldn't see any mess.

In he'd come, not seeming to notice whether it was all in order or not and start right in feeling our necks, behind our ears, the whole routine. That's when I liked him the best. He never had too much to say. He didn't feel obligated to make a lot of silly talk just because he was stuck there examining me. Once, when I was the sickest, he spoke for the first time as he left. He said to me " 'Bye, Peanut" and smiled right at me. It's not every grown-up who can make a sick child feel good inside.

Mother had left a jelly-glass in the bathroom. It was the same one I used last week. When I emerged she was waiting at the door, taut as a marathon runner receiving the team's medallion and sprinting off towards the kitchen.

Was my mother angry at me? Perhaps not in an out-and-out way. It had to do with this test. Maybe if my urine failed she'd then really be angry with me. If it passed, perhaps she would be pleased.

What was it that urine showed anyway? What were they testing for? I stood facing a wall of books, running my finger along the bindings. *The Love Letters of George Bernard Shaw to Ellen Terry. Man and Superman. Pygmalion.* There was a whole shelf of Shaw. The feeling of foreboding had returned now, not as a flash, but as a steady, monotonous gnawing. What were they trying to find out?

No, not find out, verify. Hadn't Dr. Green said that the first specimen, the one I gave last week had failed? Maybe those were not his exact words, but what he meant was that it had failed. Now he was out there in the kitchen doing a double-check on the laboratory. But he expected this one to fail too. What does it mean? Mother must know. That's why she's acting so oddly.

Maybe it has to do with that menstruation talk. Mother seemed nervous about that. She'd said that she definitely did not want me to tell my sister, Susan. She was too young and not ready for such a womanly confidence. I was the first to agree that the brat was too young. But hardly a half-hour had passed when along she comes, starting her know-it-all teasing and off I went, spilling the beans just to show her that she wasn't so smart after all. I wonder if Mother knows that I broke my promise.

Hushed voices could just barely be heard from the kitchen. The tense, hissing sound of whispered conversation. Whatever it was about was not good. Why would they whisper? Why do they leave me alone for so long? What is so awful that no one can mention in a normal voice?

Then there came the sound of a telephone being dialed. It was the one in the front hall. Dr. Green calling his office? No. It was my mother speaking again in that same tight whisper. I stared at the extension telephone which sat on a leather-top desk no more than two feet from where I stood. It would be so easy. I knew how to slip the receiver off the hook without causing the telltale click which would indicate that someone was listening. At least I might find out *something*. Why doesn't anyone talk to me?

No. If I'm already in trouble, that would make it worse. This time, I'd slip with the receiver, Mother would yell about respecting the rights of others, and whatever I'd done would be hopelessly compounded.

Instead, I turned back to the wall of matched volumes and withdrew the dictionary. Collapsing into a high back leather chair under the weight of the edition, I quickly found the word I wanted. It was as expected: not a clue, nor a hint, nor a single suggestion which might set me on the right track.

> *urine* ('rin) a fluid excretion from the kidneys into the bladder from whence it is voided through the urethra; in man it is amber-colored, with a normal specific gravity of about 1.015.

Amber-colored, specific gravity; who cared about those? The other words further down the page were less to the point. Naturally. It was the wrong book. I was stabbing blindly now. Uriniferous, uriniparous, urinogenital. I returned the book to its place, knowing that I was already convicted. What the hushed voices were deciding was what to do with me.

I sat straight and still in the leather chair, my hands folded in my lap. There is such a thing as accepting your punishment with dignity. Even if you are eleven.

When they returned, they looked as any jury would: sober,

burdened by the responsibility of the verdict they would render. Poor grown-ups.

"Ah . . . Jane . . . we . . . ah . . . have found . . . a . . . little . . . something."

I'd never heard Dr. Green stammer before. It made me feel embarrassed. I wished he'd stop. My mother was staring at me as if she expected me to disappear. Had he said "found a little something? Found out a little something?" What's a little something? They're acting like it's a big something.

"We have . . . ah . . . some reason to believe that your . . . ah . . . body . . . ah . . . may not be working exactly as it should. We're still not perfectly sure, now, you understand, but . . ." The old boy was beginning to pull out of it. As he picked up steam, the stammering lessened. Thank goodness. It was hard enough to figure out what he was telling me. My mother looked as if she'd like to faint. I wished he'd get to it.

"We would like to check further, Jane. I've arranged for a young man, a specialist over at Eighty-seventh and Park to see you today. Doctor Frederick Russell. Yes, Doctor Russell. When your father gets home, he's on his way now, you'll all go over to see him. I believe it's best if you go together." He looked at my mother who sighed and nodded.

"While we wait for your dad," said Dr. Green, a little more relaxed now, "I'd like to ask you a few questions, Jane." My heart thumped again.

"All right," I consented so softly that he may not have heard.

"Are you thirsty, Janie?"

"Yes, very."

"Do you sometimes leave your class to get a drink?"

"Yes."

"More than once in a class?"

"Yes, sometimes."

"And do you urinate frequently?"

"Well, I . . . er . . ."

"Do you have to get up in the middle of the night to void?"

"Yes." There it was again. Something about urine. The answer to all this double-talk had to do with urine. My urine.

"Dr. Green," I cried suddenly, "please sir, what's *wrong* with my urine?" He got nervous again. The minute I asked that question.

"Ah . . . well . . . ah . . . Janie, the body is a . . . ah . . . wonderful . . . a . . . mechanism . . . ah. When something is . . . ah . . . amiss . . . ah . . . it sends us signals . . . ah . . . yes, that's what they are, signals. Now your urine . . . ah . . . is sending us a signal."

"What *kind* of signal, Dr. Green?"

"An SOS, my child." He actually looked pleased with the example.

"Yes, sir, but what I mean is, what's wrong that it has to send out a signal? What is the nature of its trouble? For instance, perhaps the specific gravity is off? Or the color is not the usual amber?" It took guts to keep after him like that.

Dr. Green smiled. Never would he figure out how I happened to be aware that urine had a specific gravity in the first place.

"No," he said, still amused, "it isn't either of those." He inhaled audibly. "What your urine is telling us, Jane, is that your body . . . ah . . . is not properly using the sugar it is receiving." A flood of relief began. At last. I was beginning to hear something concrete.

"When the body . . . ah . . . does not metabolize a substance . . . ah . . . sugar, for instance, an imbalance exists, a . . . ah . . . condition . . . ah . . . which requires correction. We are not certain, but we think . . . ah . . . that this has happened to you, Janie."

"This condition, Dr. Green. Does it have a name?"

"It's called diabetes, my child."

I'd never heard of it.

CHAPTER TWO

We sat close together on the seat of the taxi as we crossed Central Park, but it was as if we were each alone. My hand, grimy under the nails from working the potter's wheel earlier today, lay on my lap only inches away from my father's, which were fleshy, with manicured fingernails and pretty white moons sticking out at the cuticle. Usually he would seize my hand in his; hold it, squeeze it, pretend that the joints were displaced, tease me about the callus from the pressure of my hockey stick. But today he paid no attention to it.

My mother loved to comment on the passing scene. She'd tell me the same things over and over since we often traveled on the same route. You did not protest any more than you would protest that you'd heard the Three Bears too often, or the Dr. Doolittle stories or Uncle Wiggly. On this day, however, she was silent. Not just silent, but in a kind of trance. It was getting to me.

We were coming to the place where she always said, "Your grandmother, may she rest in peace, went to school in that building."

Now she said nothing. When we passed the old brownstone which she had lived in when she met my father, she always said, "I left that building as a bride. All the neighbors watched from their windows and waved good-bye."

I could easily imagine the scene. Mother, right out of that pensive, eyes-down portrait which stood on her dresser, coming to life as she skillfully maneuvered the brownstone stoop. Good-bye, building. Good-bye, neighbors. The throngs waved from their windows. We were passing the famous landmark now, but Mother was silent.

It was just me and the cab driver, who was alive, but you could hardly tell. And there was the scraping wheeze of the windshield wipers as they achieved for an instant the perfection of a gleaming, wet windshield, free of the raindrop enemy, doomed only to begin again and again and again.

"What does that mean? To have diabetes?" I asked, and the whole scene came to life.

"Don't say that. You don't know that you do." My mother.

"We needn't jump the gun, Jane," my father said. "That's why we're going to Dr. Russell. He's a specialist in it. He knows a lot more than Dr. Green." He began to warm up to the idea. "Yes," he continued, "I'm not so sure *what* Dr. Green knows. Except maybe how to send out bills at the end of the month. He's very good at that. Yes honey, let's cross each bridge as we get to it. This may yet turn out to be a big mix-up. A mistake."

It was hard to concentrate. I was too thirsty. No matter what I started thinking about. I ended up dreaming of things to drink. Wild things like the raindrops off the windshield, or the horrible, muddy puddles at the curb. I was not only getting diabetes, I was also going crazy.

But I felt an unexplainable hope that things were going to work out even though nothing was making sense at the moment. OK, I was having something in my urine called diabetes, but now we were on our way to a specialist doctor who was going to fix it up. Maybe I'd have to take some pills, or get poked around. Maybe I'd have to miss school for a few days and stay in bed, but I'd surely be better by the weekend. Nancy Hill and I were going to have a sleep-over date at her house. So I decided that whatever this Dr. Russell was about to dish out, I could take because it would be worth it to be rid of all this.

✳

The new doctor's office was kind of beat-up looking, like the furniture had been used by hundreds of people daily. The rug had a path carved into it from the entrance to the waiting room. Two ashtrays were full: cigarette butts, partly smoked cigars, a gum wrapper and a piece of bloody cotton. There were lots of good magazines. We sat down together again, close, as if we were still in the taxi. There was no one around like other patients, nurses, or office people. A cleaning woman was mopping the floor in an adjacent hallway. Dr. Russell, wherever he was, had waited beyond his office hours just to see me. It was beginning to get scary again.

Then he came into the room and was shaking hands with my

parents, asking them to move over so that he could sit next to me on the couch.

"Hello, Jane. I heard all about you from Dr. Green." I think he meant good things; that he'd heard good things from Dr. Green. There was something about the way he said it. "You're at the Gate School?" He sat right next to me, his stethoscope sticking out of his jacket pocket. While he talked he pinched my arm to see how skinny I was, he looked at my palms, took my pulse, pulled down my eyelids, looked at my gums, all that in a fairly non-obnoxious way, almost as if that's what you do when you sit chatting with someone on a couch. "What grade?"

"Seventh. But we don't call them grades, we say forms. First form."

"Oh," he said, nodding. Now he was looking into my eye with that light mounted on a clicking wheel. "Look straight at that picture, please, Jane." His large, lined forehead was lightly touching mine. "Breathe out."

"Do you have a funny taste in your mouth?"

"Yes."

"What's it like?"

"Like I just finished a mealy apple. One that's overripe. Sweet. Fruity." My answer was immediate. Dr. Russell had no way of knowing that identifying tastes and smells was *my* specialty, you might say. Last summer at camp, I had been the only one to be able to identify, blindfolded, such difficult items as an avocado, a pine cone, a bay leaf and a sprig of dill. I had earned my side ten points in our color war which we lost anyway because of all the drips on the team.

"How do you feel, Jane? Thirsty?"

"Yes."

"Well, we'll fix that up. How else? Do you have a headache?"

"I guess so." I looked past Dr. Russell at my mother. She nodded at me, mouthing the words "Tell him everything."

"What about nausea?"

"I . . . I . . . Yes, that too."

"Have you vomited?"

"No." I was glad it was true. It seemed cleaner.

"When did you first notice that Jane didn't seem herself, Mrs. Goldstein?" Dr. Russell asked. He had his reflex hammer poised at my knee.

"As far back as August, I suppose," my mother said. Pow. He hit. I jumped. "But it was nothing you could put your finger on," she continued. "She'd been checked by Dr. Green before she went to camp in June. Everything was fine then."

"Was a urinalysis done at that time?"

"I don't think so," she answered. "It was just a routine examination before camp. We had no reason to suspect . . ." Mother hesitated. "When we visited her in August, she looked thinner and somewhat drawn, but otherwise she seemed well. That's right, Abe, isn't it? You thought so too."

"Yes," my father agreed. "She seemed fine. Healthy and happy. Out there in the field, hitting the ball, jumping in the lake, having a wonderful time. A kid couldn't want a more wonderful time. Why, when I was a kid, I swam in the Hudson River, Doc. But don't worry, I had a good time too, you can bet on that. You don't need a spring-fed lake in Vermont to enjoy some good, healthy fun."

"We inquired about her appetite," my mother said, getting back on the track, "but the counselors assured us that she was the hungriest eater in the group. In fact, they commented on the fact that Jane ate a second helping of almost everything served. She never even did that at home."

"Yes," Dr. Russell nodded, "that's part of the picture."

"We assumed, since there was nothing else to go on, that she was having a growth spurt . . . it happens to so many children while they're away at summer camp. It wasn't that she was just thinner. She was taller too. Of course," she added wistfully, "there were those deep black circles under her eyes. That should have told me. Jane is normally such a healthy-looking child. She turned to my father and asked, "Isn't she, dear?"

"She certainly is," he agreed emphatically, as if that would make it true. "No kid ever had such a wonderful summer, either. Not where I come from. Why she ate everything that wasn't nailed down. Between what they served her in the dining room, double helpings and all, and what I sent her from the office for nibbling, you could have fed an army." My mother gasped.

"You sent her? What did you send her?"

"Oh, whatever Schrafft's was featuring that week," he said proudly. "Cookies, candy, different bonbons, remember them, honey? Each one wrapped in that silky, colored paper?" Mother's chest heaved in a great silent sigh. At the same moment, Father paled and in a shaky whisper, said to Dr. Russell, "Oh, no. All sugar."

"That's wrong, Mr. Goldstein," the doctor spoke directly. "One cannot give a child diabetes by feeding him candy. If this were so, every child coming out of a circus tent would be a diabetic. Sugar is detrimental only when the disease is actually present."

"But if this . . . this is all true, then it *was* present when I bombarded her with candy."

"You couldn't have known then." My father looked unconvinced. "Every father likes to pick up a little treat for his children once in a while. Actually, I'm more interested in knowing something of your backgrounds. Is there diabetes in either of your families?"

"No," my father said firmly. Was he annoyed that the doctor should ask such a question?

"No," said my mother. No diabetes. Maybe it was all a mistake.

"None at all? Are your parents living? What did they die of?" It wasn't diabetes, you can be sure of that. Lots of other stuff, though. Cancer, heart attacks, asthma, allergies. But so far no diabetes.

"Your siblings? Any diabetes there?" He sure was persistent. And it paid off. My father said "No." But my mother said, "I think my brother has diabetes."

The doctor directed his entire attention towards my mother. "You *think?*" he asked. "Don't you see him?"

"Certainly, I do," said my mother, irritated.

"Well then, is he a diabetic or not?" It was a testy question, but Dr. Russell spoke the words evenly, without impatience.

"Yes, I suppose he is a diabetic. We haven't discussed it recently."

"Age of onset?"

"You mean Fred?"

"Yes, Mrs. Goldstein. How old was Fred when his diabetes was discovered?"

"Twenty-five" she said, relenting.

So Uncle Fred had diabetes and he had been discovered. It was a funny way of putting it. As if he had been having it secretly and then, one day when he was twenty-five, poor Uncle Fred got discovered. Aha! Caught. And that was what was happening to me today. I was getting discovered. Even though I was only eleven. I'd had enough of this bad dream.

"All right," the doctor said, standing and addressing himself to me. "Have you been giving lots of specimens lately?"

"One other today and one last week for Dr. Green."

"How about one for me?" We both smiled and I said, "Sure."

Minutes later he returned to the waiting room carrying a syringe with a gleaming steel needle and a wad of cotton. It was loaded with a cloudy, gray solution. Tears stung furiously. An injection was unexpected. Not in the rules. Dirty pool. I didn't want it because it would hurt.

"It won't hurt," Dr. Russell said, reading my mind. "I would tell you if there was anything to worry about. Don't worry about this." That was it. Don't worry, he said. He was pushing the sleeve of my blouse aside. Don't worry.

"Look the other way, if you'd like." I felt betrayed. To think that this man might have been my friend. A cold shock of rubbing alcohol touched my skin. I turned towards my parents. "Take it," their eyes pleaded sadly.

"Well? Was that so bad?" the doctor was asking, his arm on my shoulder. I had felt nothing. Obviously, it was over. He was rubbing the site with the icy alcohol again. But I didn't feel a bit like declaring any new truce. Let him fish for compliments on his injecting skill. I wasn't giving any. I sat in a semi-sulk as he conferred briefly with my parents. He'd see me tomorrow afternoon after school. Yes, I could go if I felt well enough. Eat normally. Save my first urine in the morning. Tomorrow they'd talk at greater length. He'd like to watch me for a day or so.

"Don't worry," he was telling them. They should call him immediately if I seemed ill. Here was his home number. Then they all shook hands, and my father thanked him, for what I don't know exactly.

"But Jane's still mad at me," he said, in good humor. I said nothing.

"I'm sure she's really not, Doctor," my mother volunteered, the traitor.

Another silence.

"That's right. I really am," I finally said, to settle it.

Going home in the taxi we discussed the demerits of a private school in which the students are encouraged to express their opinions.

✳

I reasoned, as I lay on my bed waiting for the maid to announce dinner, that I was only being let in on about one-fourteenth of what was really going on. Nothing was happening according to what I expected.

I was sick. Diabetes. My urine was sick. I was thirsty and tired and headachy and slightly nauseated, but not vomiting. I was skinny and had deep black circles under my eyes when I am usually such-a-healthy-looking-child. Somehow I am getting sick *now* from eating all that candy that Daddy sent me last summer. A remote-control delayed reaction. Eating it all myself, too. Instead of dividing it with my bunk like the note said. Crime doesn't pay.

So here I am, discovered, scared and sick with everyone around me in an absolute uproar of swallowed sobs, testing urines, taking my pulse and my autobiography and then . . . then, the greatest insult of all . . . a big, fat needle right in my arm for the supreme punishment. But this is the part that doesn't make sense: he gave me the penicillin. My fate dictated that I had to take it. Then why don't I feel better by now? I didn't. As a matter of fact, I actually felt worse than before when I was only slightly nauseated . . . not vomiting. Now, by God, I was quite nauseated and . . . yes, it certainly seemed . . . I screamed for my mother.

✳

When we gathered for dinner, the same sense of confusion plagued me. On an ordinary day, you could expect certain things to happen and they always did. It was what made my life mine, and what made me, Jane Goldstein, different from all the other kids, who, of course, had their special lives. You usually didn't give it a thought. Unless you were sitting in your own chair, at your own table, in your own dining room with the right father and mother and sister, and none of it was happening right.

Oh yes, my sister was still kicking around under the table and fooling with the silverware as she always did when we first sat down, but the air was so charged with this strange other trouble, that after a while she gave up her pestering without anybody even shooting her so much as one dirty look. My mother didn't tell me to pull the chair closer, to sit up straight, to open my napkin, to sniff out instead of up, none of those things.

Usually, my sister and I begged our father for stories about his secretary, all untrue and we knew it. They always ended with an appraisal of her daily number of typographical errors, each day's count being outrageously higher than the last. He, in turn, would inquire about the health of my Latin teacher, to whom he had taken quite a liking on the recent Father's Day. "If she wants me to come in after school to decline any nouns, just let me know," he always offered, and we would roar with laughter because Daddy, you could bet, never had Latin.

But today these rituals were not possible. We all sensed it, even Susan, who hadn't been told a thing, I'm sure. Sociability would have been offensive to my parents. It was a dreadful pall which lay on our family. Simply eating a silent meal together at one table seemed to require the utmost concentration. No one was hungry. I still felt ill enough to have no interest in the food being served and fortunately, no one pressed me to eat.

"I've had the shot. I'm getting better. Tomorrow I should be well." It repeated and repeated in my mind. Suddenly, I knew what was wrong; what made no sense. Yes, I've had the shot. But no, I don't seem to be getting any better. Could it be that tomorrow I won't be well? Is that what they're brooding about?

So I said to my father, stabbing, "Don't worry, Daddy. If I'm not better tomorrow, I'm sure that I'll be OK by Friday," which was, incidentally, the day that I had plans for a sleep-over date at Nancy Hill's. They looked at each other with alarm, my mother and father did, as if I'd said goddammit or something, and then they said nothing. Nothing.

Until the dessert came in, a mocha cake, my very favorite and my mother cut pieces for everyone except me. When I asked for mine, she again looked at my father that way. For a minute I thought I wasn't going to get any, but then Mother picked up the knife and cut me a piece that no one would believe. I mean how she got it so thin without an electric shaver is beyond me. She then put this infinitesimal sliver of my favorite mocha cake on a plate with a fork and passed it to me. IN SERIOUSNESS. And then she said, "I didn't mean to forget you, Jane, it was just that you didn't seem to be eating tonight." Whatever the struggle was really about, one thing was sure. I was losing.

It was close to bedtime when the telephone rang. Mother answered. I didn't try to beat her to it or anything because nobody in particular had said, "Call you tonight" in the hall where our steel, olive coat lockers lined the brick walls. In addition, the unrelieved bewilderment of the day's events was becoming too awful for me. It was bad enough to feel sick without also feeling sad and confused. I really didn't mind the idea of going to bed. Secretly, I still hung on to the hope that tomorrow would be better. There was surprise in my mother's voice. It was that which attracted my attention to the telephone and her conversation.

"Why yes," she was saying. "She's here. Wait and I'll get her." Obediently, Mother passed the black receiver to me. She stood very close as I began to speak, her curiosity undisguised.

"Hello?" I began. "This is Jane Goldstein speaking." Mother nodded approval. Etiquette Two. *Children should always be taught to identify themselves when speaking on the telephone.* A warm voice spoke to me. For a minute I thought it might be my uncle.

"Hello, Jane. Tell me how you're feeling now."

"W-ho, who is this?" But I already knew.

"It's Dr. Russell." He had a friendly sound to him. "Tell me how you are."

"Fine, thank you, Doctor," I said automatically.

"Well, good," he said, accenting the last word. I waited for him to say something else. He didn't.

"Would you like to speak to my mother now?" I asked.

"No," he said. "I called to speak to you." It seemed astonishing. But it was also nice. "Am I still in the doghouse?"

"No," I said smiling. There was something so appealing about the way he sounded as if he cared whether I was still angry or not. Him. The specialist. After all, either way he was still the boss. He could tell me to go jump off the George Washington Bridge and I would end up having to do it. Could I really hold a grudge? Anyway, I liked him.

I held my enthusiasm in subtle check, however, just so that he would not think that a future victory with me would be as easy as this.

I said, "I did *not* like it when you sneaked in with that penicillin injection." I suppose he was impressed by my directness, for there seemed to be a moment's confusion.

"That wasn't penicillin. That was *insulin.* Who told you it was penicillin?"

"Nobody told me anything," I said, feeling far off the trail again.

"I'll see you tomorrow in my office, Jane, and there I'll explain everything. I promise." It was worth a test. Either he was trustworthy, or he wasn't.

"Doctor? The insulin you gave me, does it cure what's wrong with me?"

"Not cure, Jane. But it helps. Don't you feel a bit better tonight?"

"No." Why didn't he give me the cure? Is he holding out or something? "I might have a lot to ask you tomorrow." I meant it as a threat.

"I'll be ready for you, Jane," he said. Was he smiling at the other end? "Four-thirty."

"Doctor?"

"Yes?"

"Do you want to speak to my mother *now?*"

"No, Jane," he said. "I called to talk to no one but you." Then he said good-bye and we hung up. Perhaps I had made a new friend, which was nice. But why would he withhold the cure?

❊

That night I went to bed at my sister's bedtime, not my own. It was my idea. I could, of course, have claimed the extra hour and a half due my seniority. There would have been no dispute. But tonight no one seemed to notice as I took one final drink of water and slipped into my French Provincial bed. We lay, Susan in her bed and I in mine, waiting for Mother to come in and turn out the light.

Our room was a coordinated snake pit of yellow flowers, green buds and don't ask me what else. Navy blue. The carpet was navy blue. The bolsters on our beds were navy blue. But don't try to sleep on them, girls. They're just for show. Our moth-eaten, but beloved pillows were kept by day in our closets. Outcasts. We were allowed to claim them only at night. Above the drapes, a valance was navy blue.

The furniture was a scratched-up brown. The rest of the room was this flowered jazz, these close little yellow jobbies with green stems running around this way, that way, on the wallpaper, on the ceiling's wallpaper, the same wild pattern in chintz bedspreads and heavily-lined drawstring window drapes. All insanely matched by some decorator maniac. The ceilings ran into the walls which ran into the drapes and on to the bedspreads. I'm telling you, if your name was Mistress Mary you had it made.

Mother finally came bursting into our room to say good-night. You could enter our room in no way but by bursting; the paint pile-up on our door was from the Year of the Flood. Daddy always reacted to the stuck door by saying that there is no such thing as a true craftsman since the painters got their union, etcetera, etcetera, on and on, but he never attempted to find a true craftsman, union or nonunion; or to be one himself by taking some paint remover to the wretched thing.

Our mother seemed distant and preoccupied. She went through the motions of getting us off to sleep automatically: drawing the heavy window drapes, kissing us lightly on our foreheads, first me and then Susan; snapping off the overhead light saying, "Good night, children dear," to which we responsively replied, "Good night, Mother" as she closed the door which then, of course, was stuck.

Mother's trancelike state was related, if not to me in the flesh, to the part of me that was sick. It caused her to treat our good-night ritual impersonally, almost as if it were necessary, but unpleasant, something to be done with. The piles of scattered clothes, the heaped bedspreads, Susan pretending to be settled down with a book sticking out from under her pillow clear as day; any one of these things would usually put Mother on the instant warpath. But tonight she carefully stepped around it all and looked the other way. I certainly could have used a good hug. Or even a good fight.

Later she returned. Much, much later. In the deepest, darkest part of the night when in order to awaken you must come up from a secret place which is warm and black and beckons you to stay. She lay next to me, her perfume, the satin of her nightgown, her arms encircling my woolie pajamas. I stirred, wondering how long she had been here.

"Mother?" I asked. Her hand stroked my head.

"Sleep, my dearest one," she answered gently.

"I can't sleep, Mother. I have to get a drink."

CHAPTER THREE

That night I almost died.

An ambulance was called. It came, breathless. "I am the angel of mercy" screamed the meticulous Red Cross, T-squared and immaculate from the vehicle's side. "Where, oh where is the angel of death?"

The attendants abandoned it, the rotating red beam casting an eerie shadow first on the mortar facade of the apartment building and then swinging across to silhouette the leafless night of Central Park. It stood unchallenged in the NO STANDING ANYTIME ZONE, directly at the entrance to our house. People came to their windows to see what was wrong.

Two men in matching uniforms came directly to my bedroom with a canvas stretcher. They lifted me on as if I weighed nothing at all. I saw my own legs, skinny white sticks with rectangular, bony clods of feet stuck to the end of them. No one commented on how awful they were. Then they wrapped me elaborately with my coat and some medicinal-smelling blankets. On top went a furry lap robe which I had on my carriage when I was a baby. It got all covered with vomit.

I hated being on the stretcher. It was insulting, that horizontal, helpless position when the rest of the world is walking proudly on its own two feet. I was permitting myself to be transported by two paid moving men like a piece of furniture or a sack of potatoes. It didn't seem a thing for a living person to tolerate. And I was still living.

As they moved me through the world, the elevator, the lobby of our building, I was doomed to look at the underside of tables, the hem of my mother's skirt, my father's pant leg, or else, face up, the wooden beams of the ceiling. Who could know of my unhappiness? No one.

My eyes closed. The effort to summon the necessary words,

which hardly would have done any good anyway, was too great. I drifted in and out of an enveloping blackness; one which reached out to cover me and then slowly to recede, as the tide surges forward and ebbs away, foaming at the water's edge.

❋

Now I was on a different stretcher, a high, flat table mounted on wheels. It had a shiny silver pole jutting into the air at the right side above my head. There were people, doctors, nurses. A mob had gathered behind my head. A few were pushing the stretcher down a hallway, some were running alongside. I had never seen any of them before. I had never seen this place. There was not one thing which looked either nice or familiar to me. I didn't know where anyone who belonged to me was. Or if I would ever see them again.

One of the navigators at the head of the table, a doctor who was pushing hard called, "Diabetic acidosis. A kid. Looks bad."

They pushed me and pummeled me. They positioned me and repositioned me and stuck needles in me, broad fat, digging needles over and over. Silent white screams of protest bounced from one wavy corridor to the opposite one. And back. And forth. The pain seared its way through the clouds of consciousness to where I was. But I could not call back to answer it. Sometimes a voice.

"Put the insulin right into the infusion."

"Yes, sir."

"Who's doing the electrolyte levels? Go and see what's keeping him."

"Yes, sir."

Suddenly I could open my eyes. I blinked, momentarily blinded by the intense glare of the fluorescent light. Fitfully, I tried to locate the source of a stabbing in my right hand. It was a steel needle, sticking only slightly out of the fair, translucent skin. The rest was imbedded in the depths of a blue vein, a delicate, unfortunate blue vein. There were yards of winding plastic tubing connecting the outpost in my hand and a bottle of clear liquid which hung upside down from the silvery pole above my head. A burp of air appeared at the neck now and then as the liquid gurgled into the narrow tubing. Now a doctor was fixing it all up, strapping a splintboard beneath my poor hand, taping it securely so that my arm was supported up to the bend in my elbow. Methodically, he fixed the tubing to my skin with two bold strokes of adhesive and finally secured the site of the needle with several other large pieces of tape and a great surge of pain.

"There," he said with pride, seeing me awake. "That more comfortable?"

"No." I said to him. "I don't want it. Take me home." Did I really speak the words or did I just think them? No one seemed to hear me. I was again beginning to ride off on the waves of drowsiness where voices reached me through an elongated tunnel, hollow, reverberating.

"Gastric lavage, sir?"

"Only if she vomits. There's not much distention here." Hands pushed at my abdomen, faraway hands. "Feel it for yourself, Smith. You too, Carr. It's usually more pronounced than this. We can spare her the tube unless she begins to vomit." More hands, pressing, pushing.

"You collect what you can from that catheter, Doctor. Is it running through all right?"

"Yes, sir."

"It will be a while before we can hope to see an improvement in the urine. Notice, doctors, the deep and labored respirations, the evidences of dehydration here and here." Pinch, pinch. Anybody could do anything. "Blood pressure low, pulse rapid and thready, body temperature low. And the characteristic odor of acetone breath." Sniff, sniff. I could hear them learning it, absorbent engorgers, out there in the brightness of their fluorescent world. Each one with a job of pushing or pressing, or sticking or testing. I was again slipping off into my soft, black place, far, far from all of this.

❊

A bell was ringing. I opened my eyes. A starchy nurse was speaking.

"Yes, Admissions. Pediatric emergency. Name? I don't know. Let me see. What's her name, Doctor? Admissions wants to know.

"Name? I don't know. Let's see here."

"Jane Goldstein," I shouted from my deep place. "Jane Goldstein. That's my name." They couldn't hear me. My own name. Nobody knew it. And they couldn't hear me.

"Ah, here it is. Jane Goldstein." He'd found it, the idiot.

"Admissions?" asked the nurse into the receiver. "I have the information for you. Jane Goldstein. Diabetic acidosis. Critical."

"Mother? You're here?"

"Of course, I'm here, baby."

"I didn't see you before."

"I know, baby, but I was here."

"And Daddy too?"

"Yes, Janie. Here I am, sweetheart. We're both here. Does it bother you to talk?"

"No, but I'm sleepy."

"I know, baby. Jane, tell me. Is there anything you want? Something for yourself?"

"Um-hum. That Nat King Cole record, the new one."

"Daddy will get it for you, honey. Today."

"Mother, take me home. They're hurting me. I don't like it here. Please take me home. Will you?"

"Tomorrow, baby. Tomorrow when the sun comes up and everything looks bright and pretty and our Janie is all better again, we'll take you home then, baby. We promise."

"Janie, did you hear Mother? Just a little bit longer and we'll take you home. You'll see, honey. Janie? Are you . . ."

"She's sleeping, Abe."

"Do you think she heard?"

"Heard what?"

"Heard you tell her that we'll take her home tomorrow? All better, yet. If she pulls through tonight, she'll not be going anywhere tomorrow."

"I know that."

"Then what'd you tell her for? She'll remember."

"Because I wanted to give her comfort, Abe. Can I do anything for the poor child's body? That's their department. At least let me try to put her mind at rest. I'm her mother."

"Yes, and *I'm* her father. I hope she didn't hear."

When I awoke the sun was shining, but I was still in the hospital. Someone was fussing about my bed, doing something which made a clinking noise, touching me at my ankles, then at my lips, now at my eyes. Somewhere nearby wagons rolled on vinyl floors, carts filled with tinkling glasses bumped as they wheeled along. I lay awake with my eyes closed, listening. I was in a new room, a different one from last night's. It was larger, quieter. Through my closed eyelids I could tell that the window was to my left, the door to my right. I opened my eyes. The person in my room was Dr. Russell, standing very close to my bed, his starched white coat scratching the skin of my arm. He was holding the only good hand I had left; the other was totally immobilized by the infusion hanging above my bed.

"For a little girl, you gave us all quite a jumping night," he said. "Let's see how this thing is doing." He jiggled the hanging bottle of clear liquid which gurgled obligingly, and then traced the tube with his finger to the vein at which the needle was planted.

"Yes, that's fine," he said.

"Were you there? With me?" He nodded gravely.

"I didn't see you."

"I'm not surprised. You were a very sick young lady," he patted my arm, "young lady."

"And now? Am I better?" Certain questions you shouldn't ask.

"We'll wait a little longer before we celebrate," he said. Weariness had etched lines into his porous skin which I had not noticed the day before. Under the flat stiffness of his sterile doctor's coat, he seemed rumpled and vastly fatigued. Could he really have worked over me the whole night through and I not know he was there at all? That was being sick, brother.

Then he said, "Your condition is improved over last night, Jane. You came here in serious trouble. But we're going to need time and lots of rest here in the hospital before we can get you back on your feet again."

I sighed and let my body be enveloped by the oddly irritating hospital bed. I was tired too, tired as if I'd spent a day on the hockey field running back and forth from one goal to the other. If he was in charge here, I'd have a number of things to discuss with him.

But now I would sleep. It could all wait.

✳

"Mother? Mother?" She wore a different dress. Maroon with a fringed scarf at the neck, a gold pin on the scarf.

"Yes, Jane? I'm right here, baby."

"Mother, they've got me in a crib. This bed I'm in is a crib. Tell them to take the sides down, Mother. I know they go down. These silver things." I grabbed at the side bars. Only one hand moved freely. The other labored under the weight of the intravenous apparatus.

"Careful, Jane. You'll unhook your IV." She pushed the switch for the nurse. A white-haired woman entered carrying a hypodermic on a square brown tray.

"Was your light on, dear?" she asked my mother.

"I just put it on," Mother said.

"Well, isn't that a coincidence? I was just coming with some in-su-lin." The nurse kind of sang it to the tune of "Hot Cross Buns." Miss Kennedy, it said on her sign.

"Please, Nurse, will you take down the sides of my bed? I don't like them up."

"Oh, sweetheart, it's better for you to be with the sides up. While you're still so sick, that is. When you're wide awake and walking around, we'll take the sides down, first thing. Now you close your pretty eyes and let this insulin do its good work."

I closed my eyes, cringing at the icy touch of the alcohol swab and then at the sting of the needle. Tears leaked out onto my cheek, salty, dripping pools into the corner of my mouth.

"There," she said. "All done. Poor little one. She's been through a lot. My girl friend, Miss Wells, was working the emergency room when they brought her in. She'll sure be happy to know that things are looking better."

"Miss Kennedy," my mother asked nicely, "is there anything we can do about Jane's bed? The sides seem to be upsetting her."

"I know," Miss Kennedy said after a moment. "I'll leave a note for Dr. Russell about it. It's really up to him anyway. If he wants to take the side bars down, down they'll go. How's that, Missy?"

It was called Passing the Buck.

✳

When I awoke much later, the side rail was gone. I immediately utilized my new freedom by dangling my arm over the side of my hospital bed, allowing it to swing a bit this way and that, exploring the intricate underside of its electrical mechanism with my fingertips. On my opposite side, the awful thing was still there. We were married, vein and bottle, attached by broad white strips of adhesive tape and winding yards of plastic tubing.

"Look out, you've got your fingers in the gears," said my father from a chair near the window. Behind him stretched the bridge to Queens, the free one, with moving vehicles creeping along like miniature models on a slow conveyor.

Probably it was still the same day, but late in the afternoon. The sky bespoke the waning November; it was a phlegmatic, steely gray, cold as the wind, a steady indifferent slab without the promise which a tiny nuance would provide. Winter, folks.

The door to my room opened with a scraping noise, one which I had heard in my sleep at some other time. How many hours had passed? Or could it have been days? My mother and Dr. Russell were entering the room, momentarily allowing in the sounds from the hall outside. Could it be that there was a whole world out there in that corridor? A busy, bustling world of rubber-soled nurses' shoes squeaking efficiently over a synthetic flooring. Someone had the job of manicuring that floor with a whirring machine in the smallest hours of the night. Who? What emergency was causing those white-stockinged legs to rush past my door? Who was in trouble down the hall? An even female voice spoke with professional neutrality into the loudspeaker system: "Dr. Brown, Dr. George Brown, Dr. Brown. Dr. Shutter, Dr. Shutter." Then she went back to Dr. Brown again, "Dr. George Brown, Dr. Brown."

Now the door scraped closed and again my room became an isolated place, far removed from the action in the outside corridor. I wished I were out there instead of in here. My mother and Dr. Russell were wearing different outfits of clothing than they had the last time I saw them. Had they changed, as in a fashion show? Or was it a different day? A vase of flowers, great white mums, stood on a bureau in the corner of the room. What was in the bureau? My things? Anyone's things?

My father and Dr. Russell were shaking hands. Father was thanking him for some kind of room change.

"I would have preferred to have kept her in the pediatric ward," Dr. Russell was saying. "They handle problems of this type every day. They know the best ways of making children comfortable in a hospital. The children benefit from seeing one another. The overall situation is far better, in my opinion. But if you feel that this is so much more to your liking . . ."

"Much, Doc," my father assured him. "This is much more like it. I don't want Jane in any ward. Not when I can afford to give her a decent room. A child likes a private bathroom and shower, just like a grown-up does." I wondered where this bathroom and shower was. And I wondered why he was worried about whether I had one or not. Surely he could see that I was rigged up to my bed so securely that I couldn't even turn over, much less use the john. Perhaps *he* wanted to take the shower.

"The other thing, Mr. Goldstein," said Dr. Russell, "is that we happen to have two other diabetic children in the hospital at the moment. It's a coincidence which could be used to great advantage in the days to come when we hope to teach Jane what she needs to know as a diabetic. Some of the routines and disciplines. Children usually respond well in a group. They could help each other to understand and follow the program which we outline. They could be friends. There are some very lonely moments in every hospitalization, you know. Particularly for a child."

"I know, Doctor," my father answered. "That is exactly why I want her up here on the private floor. No rigid rules about when you can visit your own child . . ."

"They're quite reasonable in Pediatrics, Mr. Goldstein. Parents are permitted to stay for almost the entire day. You can do everything except sleep there."

"That's okay for those kids, Doc," my father insisted. "For Jane, I like a nice, quiet room. No drafty three, four, five bed ward with a lot of sickly kids for roommates. If Jane needs company, she'll be able to talk to the ones who know best how to care for her. Her mother and father. She can hardly be lonely when we're here with her all day. Right? And by the way, Doctor," he continued, "I'd like to get that telephone taken out of here. The child doesn't need that constant ringing to disturb her." I looked at the telephone for the first time. It had not made a single sound since I had been here.

"Simply unplug it," Dr. Russell said quietly. I knew that instead of being solicitous, my father was being difficult. The doctor seemed to be taking a minute to catch his breath. Then he said that he wanted to examine me, would they please wait down the hall in the reception room? My mother and father paused for a minute, as if considering whether to grant his request. When they had decided favorably, they then moved out the door, my father patting the bureau as he went, murmuring that what every patient needed was a place to show off his flowers.

※

"The first thing we'll do," Dr. Russell said, beginning to pull at the wide strips of tape on my hand, "is to get rid of this thing." Deftly, the doctor clamped off the liquid flowing through the transparent tube and removed the needle from my hand. A swollen, bruised lump of a vein showed through my skin. Then he freed me from

the adhesive and the board. I had been bound for so long that my
arm still assumed the same position, only now without support.

"Move it like this," he demonstrated. "It's stiff from being in the
same place. How about some real food, Jane? Are you hungry?"

"I am. Yes. No one's brought me any food since I've come here.
Don't they bring you food in hospitals?"

"They do, Jane. It's just that up to now, I've wanted to get you
well enough to eat again by mouth. We were feeding you, you
know, through this tube in your arm. Not exactly steak, eh?" We
laughed. "You feel hungry because the insulin is working to bring
down your blood sugar level. When your blood sugar level is
normal, you will feel hungry three times a day. By the time you go
home, we hope to have you on an insulin program which will allow
you to eat at the same time as the rest of your family. With perhaps one extra snack before you go to bed."

I nodded at the doctor. "Is he kidding?" I thought. "When *else*
do you eat besides three meals and an extra snack? What's so hot
about that?"

"It's like a puzzle that we have to solve, Jane. While you're here,
we have to figure out how much insulin you need and how much
food you can eat at that dose of insulin. All the while, we have to
keep your blood sugar levels within the acceptable range. You get
it? It's sometimes quite a problem. Like the other night, your blood
sugar went so high that you became very ill and we had to bring
you here in an ambulance. It's taken us three days to begin to
straighten you out. Naturally, we want to avoid extreme episodes
like that if we possibly can."

"This is what diabetes is? I asked.

He nodded. "Want to sit up?" He pushed a button at the end of
my bed and slowly I began to be bent into a sitting position accompanied by the special music of an electronic hum.

So it had been three days. Lost. And this was the first time I was
sitting up, seeing the world, the room, this place. On a foot stool
lay new fluffy blue bedroom slippers. Neatly. Side by side. Whose
slippers were they? Mine? The last patient's? Had she died?

"You don't get better from diabetes, do you Dr. Russell? You
just always have it, day after day after day. Right?" I don't know
how I knew, but I knew.

"Right, Jane. It's called a chronic illness. It doesn't get better if
you're thinking of being cured. But it will be better in the sense

that you will feel well most of the time after we straighten you out here in the hospital. You'll go back to school and do all the things that the other children do, play games, take tests, go to dances."

I said "Oh." He had apparently expected me to applaud at the news that I could play sports, take tests and go to dances. But I had never once thought that I might not be able to play sports, take tests and go to dances. What was there to be so happy about? I was a few steps behind. At least.

"We'd like you to try to use the bathroom now," said the doctor. "You're well enough. But please call the nurse to walk you there for the rest of today. People sometimes get a little wobbly when they've been off their feet for a few days. Let her help you for the first few times. She'll want to show you what to do about testing, anyway."

"Testing?"

"Your urine, Jane. That's a part of having diabetes that will become second nature to you. I need to know how much sugar is present in each urine specimen you pass. That is one way that I can judge how much insulin you need for that day. So I will ask you to save every urine. And the nurses here will teach you how to make the test you need. Then you will write down the results and tell them to me. I'm sure you are smart enough to be able to do it accurately."

I agreed with some interest. "I'll call for the nurse when I'm ready," I said.

"You'll have a meal sent in to you for dinner tonight," he said, getting ready to leave. "Be sure to eat it all, now."

"Don't worry," I answered. "I told you I was hungry."

He smiled. "I'll be in tomorrow morning and we'll see how things are coming along." Then he left. I guessed that he spent a few minutes talking to my parents in the hall. In my valuable moments alone, I looked out over the East River through my large, private window at the beautiful blackness of the night. Tiny lights of cars twinkled on the bridge. I was glad to be sitting and seeing things again.

When my mother and father returned to my room, they appeared to have been arguing with each other. It was a familiar way that they had; of returning from a furious battle, chilly and polite, acknowledging the other only when necessary. It was, I think, to convince my sister and me that we lived in a model home, everyone of genteel inclination, honest as George at the cherry tree, and no fried foods. Of course, Susan and I knew from the beginning that parents have their own fights. Sometimes we created our own dramatic workshop by planning the complicated ways in which we would keep in touch when our home was dissolved and we were placed in different orphanages.

"Look," I said, holding my free arm high for inspection, "no more drip."

"Good," said my mother. They were sitting around my bed.

"Good riddance to that thing," said my father. Nobody seemed too happy.

"I'm sitting up," I ventured. "I'm to have dinner tonight. Dr. Russell says I'm getting better now."

"Better, yes. But you'll still have diabetes. That's not like really getting better. It's a chronic illness. That means it doesn't go away."

"But he says that it won't be so bad when he figures out how much insulin I need. Then I'll be able to do all the things the other kids do." Nobody seemed too happy about this, either. I invoked the doctor's words, hoping for some magical effect. "I'll be able to play games, take tests, go to dances . . . anything at all."

"What does he do? Learn a script? He gave us that speech." My father was furious. It was scary. "That Russell needs to learn what part of the job is his and what part is mine. He can put the kid on her feet with all the drips and needles he needs. After that, I'll be the one to decide how happy I should be that my kid can play games. Games." He snorted. "Everyday, ordinary games. Like every kid alive plays. I should be happy that my kid can maybe play them? Maybe, if this test comes out right and that dosage is measured correctly?"

"Abe, please," said my mother.

"Don't you 'please' me," he returned. "That doctor's going to learn what's in his province and what's in mine. Like with this room. He wants her in some pediatric ward where she wouldn't get a decent night's sleep with all those other diabetic kids crying all the time. Well, I won't have it. I like a place with a dresser for your clothes."

"Are my clothes in that dresser?" I was wearing a funny white pair of pajamas that tied closed, but not very well. The name of the hospital was stamped in black ink in several places.

"No, honey," my mother said. "They're home. That dresser's empty, Abe."

"I don't care if it is empty," my father said. "I just want it to be there." That was the end of that. I wondered why the other diabetic children cried at night. Did they hurt them? At night when nobody was around? Would they hurt me, too? Or just the children who were in the ward?

"Tell her," my mother said to my father.

"Tell her what?" He had lit a big cigar.

"About not telling anyone."

"Yes, Janie," he said, springing into action again. "This business of having diabetes, I want you to know that this is a *private* affair. It's something that is nobody's concern except yours and mine and your mother's. There's no need for anyone else to know about it. There would be no purpose in telling anyone else." My mother then took over.

"We're the only ones who have your best interest at heart, Jane. All the others, they may seem to care about you now, but feelings people have for each other change from year to year."

I thought about my friend Margie. Mother knew, for she said, "Remember how you and Margie spent every day after school together last year, how you told each other everything and were the very best of friends?" I nodded. "Well, now you and Margie are at different schools and you haven't seen her in over a month. Margie probably has lots of new friends, just as you have. She's most likely with one of them right now, maybe telling her the most special secrets she knows. Maybe even yours." She looked at my father. "I think Jane is getting too old for that kind of stuff anyway, Abe. That's really for babies. And Jane is now in junior high school." I thought of Margie. I still loved her. I couldn't believe that she'd be doing that. But I also felt worried. Mother knew a lot. She was hardly ever wrong.

"That's why we don't want you to tell anyone, Jane," Mother continued. "Not your friends, or your teachers, not our relatives or anyone else we know. Because all they would do is feel sorry for you. And you don't need anyone to feel sorry for you. People should like you for the terrific kid you are, not because they know you're sick. We don't want anyone saying behind our backs, 'Poor Jane Goldstein, she's got diabetes.' Let them feel sorry for their own kids, not for you."

"Yes," my father said. "When people meet you on the street, do we want them saying, 'Doesn't Jane Goldstein look pretty today considering she's a diabetic?' We want them to take you for what you are, and say 'Look at Jane Goldstein. My how pretty she looks.' You don't want people feeling sorry for you, do you?"

I didn't. No. But I also felt stunned and confused by the unity of their attack; by their desperation that I see their point; not just see it, but embrace it, leap upon it. The very sound of what they were saying was frightening to me. If there was any logic, it would be lost. My father asked me again, this time with some impatience, whether I would enjoy having people feel sorry for me. Could I be considering such a state of affairs? Or was my attention simply falling off?

"No," I finally said. "I don't want that." Then I asked, "Can Susan know?" My parents exchanged confused looks for a minute. They hadn't decided this one yet.

"Yes," said my mother after a pause. "Susan will be told when she's mature enough to respect our confidence. That may not be right away, however." My guess was about four years from now.

"You may have wondered why we wanted the telephone unplugged," Mother went on. "It's basically for the same reason. There's no need for all those vultures to smack their lips over the details of this. True, you're in the hospital," she said as if reciting a line from a play. "With pneumonia. Not too serious a case; you'll be back to school in a week or so. But no visitors, no telephone calls. No disturbances of any kind. Doctor's orders."

"But I don't have pneumonia."

"We know you don't," came the reply, "but they don't have to know it. People are used to pneumonia. It's something familiar. Anyone can get pneumonia. Right, Abe?"

"Right. In '29 lots of *healthy* people died of pneumonia."

I looked at my parents, intense, troubled, calling instructions to me through a screen of panic. And then I thought of something funny. Ironical. A backfiring joke. The dresser did have something in it after all. It was the black telephone, absent from my bedside table, silent, its wire with the four-pronged jack at the end. That was what was in the dresser, bottom drawer. I said to my father, "On the children's ward, you'll never see a dresser with a telephone in it."

And he said to me, "Yes, but you see people. And people talk."

*

Then the aide brought dinner, my first meal since I came to the hospital. I was honestly hungry and the anticipation of food suddenly occupied all my energy. The details of the distribution of food in an institution had always fascinated me. I liked to look into the school cafeteria early in the morning when the workers were just arriving, seeing the big truck containing the day's supply back up to the kitchen, watching them unload crates of individual milks for our afternoon snack, the great bins containing bread for our sandwiches. I liked to watch the people who prepared our food and then later served it to us at our assigned tables, to see them in their own clothes before they put on their waitress costumes with the sanitary, protective hair coverings.

The waitresses were generally a subdued lot on the job, rarely making any personal contact with the different shifts of students who exploded in and out in response to a nerve-wracking buzzer system. "Please kids, don't throw your peas on the floor. I got a bum ticker," was the only intimate information which Mary, the waitress for my table, had provided. But she so appealed to us with this personal touch, that we banded together and decided to cut it out with the peas.

Now with much clatter in the hall, dinner was coming. I was a child who had not eaten by mouth for three days and the prospect was nothing less than thrilling. First my door flew open with a great creak and was held in place by an aide who knew just what to do with the brass floor-stopper. The corridor outside my room was now wide open to me. I leaned forward to try to see it all. People scurried by my door. They looked in at me sitting up in my hospital bed. I looked out at them. Often they smiled in. A woman who looked like a grandmother passed by and waved at me. I waved back.

"Really, we'll have to ask for a screen," said my mother.

The aide moved a cart containing trays for many patients to a spot right in front of my open door. There were four separate shelves of trays. She was looking for something. It was giving her difficulty. My tray, of course. She couldn't find it. I strained forward, watching. Now she was peering at the trays on the bottom shelf of her wagon. She nearsightedly examined the nameplate on my door.

"You Goldstein?" she asked. She seemed to anticipate an error.

"Yes," I said quickly. I sensed that she didn't believe me.

"Diabetic?" I nodded. She shrugged.

"Here's yours," she said quickly, picking a tray off the bottom shelf.

The aide adjusted a bedside table above my legs. Mother went to raise my bed to its highest sitting position. My father was smacking the pillows behind my bed. Everyone was happy that my meal had arrived.

"Have a nice dinner, now, honey," said the aide, smiling. "Want the door open or closed?"

"Open," I said.

"Closed," said my father. The lady closed it.

The dinner was in three sections. It was set up on an ordinary brown cafeteria tray with a place mat. It said, in script, "Good Evening." The silverware came in a transparent paper container, the salt and pepper, in one-portion disposable shakers. Like on an airplane. I could hardly wait.

There was a glass of milk and an orange out on the open part of the tray. The main course lay under a silver dome, a cover to keep the food hot. I was especially excited about seeing a cover on the main dish. It reminded me of delicious meals I'd had at parties held in hotels, at a banquet-luncheon I once went to, at a camp reunion. To the right of the covered dish stood a silvery clamp, a place-marker, with a bright pink card listing my name, my room number, and in the upper right hand corner, the word "Diabetic."

"Come on," urged my father. "Don't just stare at it. Eat."

I removed the cover by hooking it onto the first joint of my index finger through a convenient center hole. Then I stared at my meal. It was hard to believe. Tears welled and receded, alternately blurring my vision and then clearing it, allowing me to see just enough to want to cry again.

There was a potato. A shiny, boiled potato, not large, not small; fair enough. Then there was a tiny piece of wilted broccoli. Okay, a green vegetable. Finally, there was an enormous portion of a bony, whitish, disgusting-looking fish. Fish was my worst food. I hated it.

"What's . . . what's the matter?" asked my mother. She knew.

I shook my head. The disappointment was insurmountable. I was going to be crushed by it. Why did they do this? Didn't it count to them that I let them stick needles into my front, my back, my bottom, my top, wherever they fancied, whenever they chose? Did I bite them, kick them, claw them, scream for them to stop? Did I knock the hypodermics out of their horrible hands, toss the pills out the window, set fire to the curtains?

What kind of a subtle torture was it to feed me nothing, nothing except water through a tube in my vein for three whole days and then, when I am ravenously hungry, like a wild animal, serving me a piece of bony, nauseating, diarrhea-looking fish?

My father said, "Just a minute, Jane. Just wait. Hold on. Don't cry. I'll see what can be done about this meal." I leaned back into my pillows, replacing the silver dome of a lid. The meal looked better with the cover on.

I knew that it would be hopeless. My father would make a loud fuss, but in the end someone important would tell him, "I'm sorry, Mr. Goldstein, but fish it is. We take our orders from the Chief Dietician of the Universe; that's not like it was simply the Chief Dietician of the World you know. If it were only a question of going against *his* orders, why then it wouldn't be such a difficult matter. But you understand, this is different."

A nurse entered the room. My father said, "Look, Nurse, this meal that my daughter has here, it's totally unacceptable. She doesn't like fish and the potato and that tiny piece of broccoli look as if they've seen better days. Can you get her something else? A piece of meat, maybe?"

"Oh, I'm sorry, Mr. Goldstein," the nurse said sweetly to my father. Her voice was patient, measured in neat little phrases, as if one were explaining something to a very young child. "The kitchen is closed now. And anyway, Mr. Goldstein, your child is a diabetic. We never substitute on the prescribed menu for a diabetic unless we have the approval of the attending doctor *and* the dietician." There it was. Exactly as I thought.

"Do you mean to tell me that in order for this kid to get some dinner after not being fed for three days, I have to run around in the streets looking for a place where I can buy her a sandwich? Do you know that I'm paying fifty dollars a day here? It's a little ridiculous, don't you think?" She didn't think.

"I mean nothing of the sort, Mr. Goldstein," said the nurse. Cool, unruffled. "The food served to a diabetic is weighed carefully in our kitchen. Every ounce of protein, of carbohydrate, is recorded in writing. It is the only way we know to control the disease; balancing a measured food intake with a measured amount of insulin. If you make haphazard substitutions, you might as well take her home, Mr. Goldstein, remove her from the hospital entirely." Yes, Daddy, do it, do it. Take me home, make haphazard substitutions. Give her a piece of your mind. "It would be defeating your own purpose," she concluded.

The clear logic of it all, so sensibly explained by this iceberg of a nurse, lost me my sandwich, a turkey on rye with Russian dressing and cole slaw; lost me my father who was now convinced that the sandwich would have killed me; and left me with my untouched tray and that cold, disgusting piece of fish lying there daring me not to choke on its many small bones.

"Miss Goldstein," asked the nurse, "is there anything on your tray that you are willing to eat?" The milk had a ring around the top of the glass from standing so long. So I said, "The orange."

I wondered if the turkey sandwich would have killed me. Oh God, what kind of a disease was this?

"Good. You need some sugar to balance off the insulin you've had today. An orange has natural sugar in it. That's a good choice." Was she praising my selection? Was she saying that I was beginning to catch on? That I would make it as a diabetic? The orange happened to be *it*. There was nothing else on that tray that I could put into my mouth of my own free will. I sighed. The orange.

"Tomorrow," said the nurse, "I'll see to it that the dietician comes to see you, Miss Goldstein. She'll ask you what kinds of things you like more than others and she'll write it all down. Then when they make up your trays in the kitchen, they can look at her list and know what to send you that you'll like. How's that?"

"That's wonderful," jumped my mother. It seemed to me that she got happy a little too fast.

"All right," I conceded to the nurse.

"Then you'll never have fish unless you order it yourself," she said in triumphant farewell.

Somehow I doubted it.

CHAPTER FOUR

"*Good* morning, Jane. In-su-lin."

God. It was her. Hot Cross Buns. The singing commercial. Getting ready to stab the living daylights out of me. Beat it, lady. Get.

"Go away," I said. "I don't want it."

"You don't have to bother waking up," she said cheerily. "Just roll over. I'll be done and out of here before you can say 'Jack Robinson.' "

"No."

"Why not? Insulin's not a painful injection."

"Then *you* take it." I pulled the covers tightly around my neck. If she wanted to give it to me, let her inject my face.

Another day in this place off to a flying start. Today I knew where I was, all right. In the hospital. I also knew where I wished I was. At home. Other kids get kept at home when they get sick. Like my sister, for instance. And the kid downstairs who broke his leg and his mother had to wheel him around in a baby carriage like he was four months old. *They* didn't get sent to any hospital.

But when you get diabetes everybody deserts. Run. The plague. Quick, put her in the hospital.

"All right," said the nurse. "Then get up."

"What?"

"Get up. Get out of bed. Give me a urine specimen." I watched with growing suspicion as she carefully replaced the poised hypodermic across a small brown tray on my bureau. Could I have won one? That easily? I struggled into my stained flannel bathrobe and the furry blue slippers which Mother had brought while I was in the coma.

"Let me know when you're ready," the nurse called after me. "I'm going to teach you how to test your own." I eyed the syringe waiting on the dresser and headed for the bathroom. I had to face it. I was her prisoner.

I never saw more junk on one tray. There was a test tube with a clamp on it, a glass eyedropper, two jars filled with some speckled tablets, tape, a pencil, and some paper. Nurses seemed to bring everything on little trays. Like the waitress at the drive-in.

She taped a chart to the bathroom wall next to the mirror. It had my name written on it and then it had all the days listed with four blank spaces next to each one. The chart began with today's date and went all the way down the page for about six month's worth. My heart sank. Were they planning to keep me here for that long? The possibility was too terrible. Maybe they mean to give it to me when I go home. As a kind of party favor.

Miss Kennedy was dipping the dropper into the glass jar containing my urine. "Always try to have your equipment clean, Jane," she said in a teacher's voice. "Foreign material in the test tube, for example, could cause a false negative. Or, for that matter, a false positive."

I tried to look bright and interested. My shining pupil face. Which was better? A false negative or a false positive? Forget it, Goldstein. If you don't learn it today, dummy, you can learn it tomorrow. It's a chronic disease, remember? Never goes away. Not one minute off for good behavior.

"After you put five drops of urine into the test tube," Miss Kennedy was saying, "count out ten drops of water. Then take one of these tablets," she said, demonstrating, "and put the top back tightly. They spoil easily with exposure to air."

She did just what she told herself. "Now ready?" she asked, getting excited. I didn't say too much. But she didn't even notice. Not ole nursie.

"Here we GO" she squealed, letting the tablet, obviously some kind of chemical, fall dramatically into the waiting test tube. Houdini couldn't have done it better. A furious foaming began the minute the pill hit the liquid. Steaming white bubbles. A cloud of smoke. I'm telling you, everything but the Genie.

The thing was boiling away like a real Mount Vesuvius. Colors were appearing briefly at the bottom of the tube: blue, green, shades of brown, and finally a bright orange. I looked at the chart which Miss Kennedy had placed on the bathroom wall. It contained a square of each color that the liquid had turned, along with a legend.

Dark blue	Negative
Blue green	Trace
Green	Plus One +
Khaki	Plus Two ++
Tan	Plus Three +++
Orange	Plus Four ++++

Anybody could see mine was the worst. Miss Kennedy shook her head. But the lesson wasn't over yet. She said to me, "Wait until the boiling stops completely and then take a dropperful of water and add it to the tube. It makes the results easier to read." She did it. The bad news was still there, staring at us both.

"Then," she continued, "take the test to the color chart and see what color matches the one in the tube." I wasn't exactly holding my breath. She started the test tube at the first color in the left hand corner, blue. No, the bright orange didn't fit with the blue. So she moved it along, like a local train which can not miss a single station, from blue to the greens to the brown and finally, inevitably, to the last color, the unequivocal evidence of diabetes rampant, the orange. Plus four.

She didn't like it, seeing that orange result at last. The lesson was now over. We'd had our little fun. It was now back to business. Serious business. "That's bad. Plus four," she said. "We'd better let the doctor know. Back to bed now," she said, giving me a little push in that direction. "Oh yes, Jane. Look here." Now she had changed her mind. She was calling me back again. "You should always record the results of your test in writing. On this chart, please. Like this." Even if I'm dying and should be in bed? She took the pencil and wrote emphatically in the column labeled A.M.: ++++. Now she looked at me closely, perhaps for the first time.

"Do you feel all right?"

"Fine," I said. But what else could I answer? If I had said "No, not fine. Sick," it would ring the alarm which would bring the whole emergency team racing in, attacking with their needles, drips, and their rabid poking.

"You couldn't feel fine," Miss Kennedy said surely. "Not with four plus sugar in your urine. "Get into bed," she ordered. "On the double."

She grabbed the syringe from its resting place and landed it on my arm before I had a chance to jump away. "That's for now," she said briskly, swabbing the site of the needle with cotton. "I wouldn't be surprised if I'm back in three minutes flat with another dose for you. Plus four. That's very bad, little girl."

She was right, of course. In a few minutes she was back with another one. "Sorry, kiddo. Tough luck," said her eyes, as she straightened my sheets afterward. But her mouth said nothing.

✳

"We have your breakfast here, Jane, but there's a hold on it." Miss Kennedy leaned her head and shoulders into the doorway.

"What's a hold, Miss Kennedy?" A sausage? A muffin? A curse from the Wicked Witch?

"It means that your tray is here, but we have to hold it until we get an order to release it. You see? HOLD."

I saw. It meant that my breakfast was here. Yea. But I couldn't have it. Boo. That there was a lot of good stuff on it. Yea. But it would be all mouldy and rancid by the time I got it. Boo. Oh yes, I understood, all right.

I said, "The release, Miss Kennedy. What has to happen before the breakfast gets released?" I almost began to cry right here. The day had been terrible enough. And there were still about sixteen hours to go. I was hungry. Was that a crime? It was important to me. "Please, Miss Kennedy," I wanted to say in my plaintive-tragic voice, "I'm hungry."

"They're coming to do a fasting blood sugar on you. After that you can eat." I felt encouraged.

"When will that be?" I asked. Maybe right away. Any minute. Miss Kennedy looked at her watch.

"Not until nine o'clock, I'm afraid. When the Private Service Lab opens and the technicians come in." Perhaps she could sense my disappointment. "Hungry? Poor thing. I don't blame you. It's the one way that the private patients have it worse than on the wards. If you'd been on Pediatrics, the intern would have done your blood sugar early and you'd be sitting there munching away right now. But up here you have to wait till the technician gets around to you, and sometimes they're a mighty slow-moving lot."

She leaned her body on the frame of the door. "I'll see to it that they take you first when they open up," she promised. "But it'll still be nine o'clock, my chick-a-dee. Maybe you'd better settle down and go back to sleep until then," she said, coming into the room now. "Can't see what good it'll do to lie here fussing about it. Won't bring 'em here any quicker."

She was lowering the shades on the long rectangular window which had just begun to shine with the shy brightness of cold November. The room was dark again. At the edges of the window cover, daylight fought its way in. "Your tea won't be cold, you know," Miss Kennedy said softly. "I'm seeing to it personally." I turned my face away from her.

"I wanted *coffee*, not tea," I said, hateful. She seemed amused.

"Oh you did, did you? I didn't know eleven-year-olds were allowed to drink coffee."

"Well, you didn't know," I said. "But my parents allow me." She didn't believe a word.

"Take it up with the dietician," she said lightly. "Meantime, I'll keep the tea warm. In case you change your mind."

I closed my eyes. A fasting blood sugar. It sounded like a beaut.

✳

I hated her the minute she walked in. That's right. She never stood a chance with me. In she waddled, smiling. The nerve of her. Complete with her white coat and a Little Red Riding Hood basket of goodies like rubber tubes, real swell sharp needles, balls of cotton, and rubbing alcohol. Maybe she would swallow a little.

Also, there were lots of test tubes to catch all the guess what . . .? Blood of me. To top it all off, she had a hairy wart, weighed two hundred pounds stripped, wore ugly teacher shoes and a wedding ring that I didn't like. Her total score was a big, round zero.

"Morning." She shuffled toward my bed, her basket of torture swinging merrily on her arm. "Got to get a little blood from you."

Blood. It was horrible. Where do you get blood? From a cut, a stab, an accident. From me. You have to open a person's skin to get blood. You have to hurt them, injure them, kill them. Me. Always me. Jane Goldstein. Human blood bank. Living pincushion. Why?

She tied a piece of rubber tubing around the upper part of my right arm. It was exactly at the place where you'd watch if someone was bragging about their big muscle. "Make a fist, please," she said to me. She held my arm straight down and prodded at the veins with her fingers.

"Not much to work with," she muttered.

"Something wrong?"

"They're small and a lot of them are collapsed. It's from having so many infusions."

"Oh." I was hoping she'd leave. Rained out. No ball game. "Then you can't take my blood?"

"I can try," she said and plunged the razor-sharp needle into my skin. I knew that the initial pain would be worst. I thought about this. I knew that there would follow a group of other, not-so-terrible pains while the needle was being situated into the vein itself. I thought about this. I knew that once the technician had the thick, black redness backing into her collection tube, it would soon be over. I thought about this.

But the pain schedule was not working out properly. The stabbing continued, each time bringing a fiery blast of agony which was more overpowering than the last.

"Dammit," said the ugly witch through clenched teeth. "I can't get it." She tried again.

"It's enough," I whispered to her, pleading. It was hard to breathe.

"Got it," she said suddenly, snapping off the rubber tourniquet from my upper arm. "Open and close your fingers." I did. The battle was now almost over. My blood was slowly filling a large syringe.

I sighed and closed my eyes for a moment. "Some people faint at the sight of their own blood," she offered. It wasn't the blood. Brother, if I'd lived through her trying to get into a vein, then I could stand the sight of what all the pain was about. I was happy to see my blood. It meant I'd soon be rid of her.

She withdrew the syringe and pressed the site hard with a cotton ball. Then she bent my arm in half so that my hand was resting on my right shoulder and said, "Keep your arm in that position for about ten minutes and you won't be black and blue. All right?"

"All right," I answered.

"You sure were a tough one," she said, leaving. "Sorry."

I lay back in bed, my arm obediently bent, wishing for darkness and stillness and a fairy godmother who would keep me from having diabetes.

✳

It was on my breakfast tray, under the silver stand with my name
and room number on it. I spotted it instantly; a white envelope
with my name written in a kind of script called the Palmer
Method. I tore it open and read the message, carefully written with
the same curling letters.

JANE GOLDSTEIN: WE KNOW YOU'RE THERE. PLANNING REVOLUTION.
                    GIVE CONTACT QUARTER.

                                                   STUCK-UP TWO
                                                   PEDIATRICS

I read it again with a mounting sense of excitement. Stuck-up
two. Pediatrics. Of course. The two diabetic children; the patients
of Dr. Russell's. What simple tools they must be. Stuck-up two.
Real fourth-grade humor. But planning a revolution. That takes
cunning, guts. Maybe they're older. Like in third term high school.
Wow. I wished I could see them, talk to them, plug in my forbidden telephone and call them up.

I could hardly wait for the woman who had delivered my dinner
to return for the tray. It figured. She would be the contact. I
watched without patience for the minutes which had to pass. She
was giving me time to eat my dinner.

Then she returned, acting, in true spy tradition, as if she knew
nothing. She picked up my tray and headed for the door.

I called after her, "Are you the contact?"

"Huh?" she asked, balancing the tray to turn to me.

"The contact. Are you the contact?"

"No, honey, I'm just an aide," she answered, closing the door
behind her.

"Drat," I thought. "The plot is not simple." But death, destruction, and defeat to the enemy, nevertheless. It was a thrilling turn
of events.

CHAPTER FIVE

Mother had come to the hospital from the beauty salon. Her head was a beyond-belief mass of plastered half-moon hairy things which were glued about her face and neck by this faggy Monsieur Loo-ey, who has never been closer to France than Coney Island.

Once in a weak moment, I allowed Mother to take me to him. "*Do* something with this child's hair," she had said to him, like it was some kind of emergency with blood running all around. You could see from his expression of horror that he agreed that she had brought me there just in the nick of time. Five more minutes of me with my hair walking on the streets of New York would have been too late.

He then took out his little scissors with the razor attachment and did something to me, but what it was, I'm too well-bred to describe. When I left, he looked more like a girl than I did. And when I had come in, we were about even. So much for eight dollars, not counting the cab fare.

Even though Mother's hair looked like she was being prepared for mummification, she really was a nice old girl after all and had stopped in a toy store on the way to pick up this little fortune-teller for me. It really hit the spot, since in hospitals they don't exactly show movies to keep the patients busy. This take your injection—test your urine jazz was as definitely becoming dullsville.

The thing was a little crystal ball setup, really very neat, where you asked the genie a question, turned the crystal ball a full circle, and through the phony mist appears the answer to the question. Obviously, you had to limit your questions to the "yes" or "no" type, although for the greedy, there were a few other less decisive answers thrown in, like "doubtful," "sometimes," and "ask again later."

"Dietician's here to see you, Jane" said Miss Kennedy, and in walked a skinny Chinese lady in a white uniform with a name-tag which read, get this, Miss Jew.

I quickly tucked my fortune-teller under the sheet in such a way so only I could still see the answers as they floated to the top of the globe. It was hidden from those in the room, like Miss Jew the dietician, for example. I was asking, as I was interrupted, the question, "Does Artie like me?" and although I would prefer not to discuss who Artie is right now, it certainly was an important question. The answer appeared: SOMETIMES. Feh.

"Miss Goldstein?" she asked, placing herself squarely at the end of my bed, "I am Miss Jew, the hospital dietician. I would like to ask you some questions about what foods you like to eat." You could see that my mother was thrilled.

"How do you do, Miss Jew?" she asked with nothing short of ecstasy. I guess she felt related because we were Jewish.

" . . . er . . . yes, how do you do, Mrs. Goldstein?" she asked my mother. "Isn't it lucky that you are here too? I'm sure you can be of help." She smiled at my mother and then at me, showing even white teeth which were really quite pretty. She wasn't so bad, this Miss Chinese Jew. I twisted my wrist under the covers to rotate the fortune-teller, silently asking "Does he like Daphne better?" DEFINITELY NO. Well, that was a relief.

"Let's start with breakfast, Miss Goldstein. What are some of the things you like for breakfast?"

"Orange juice." She nodded and wrote it down.

"And which cereal? Do you like oatmeal? Cream of Wheat?" No, I didn't like any of those hot cereals, with the lumps. I had sent some really bad-looking stuff back on my tray this morning. You'd think she'd have noticed it.

"No," I said. "I don't like any hot cereal." Period. She nearly fainted. A radical. Eleven years old.

"You don't like any of them? Not Cream of Rice? Hot Ralston?" Nope. Sorry, baby. Who could believe it? I was a living freak. My mother shrugged her shoulders.

"She doesn't," Mother finally vocalized. But Miss Jew was basically a good sport, you could see that. And she wasn't going to be so easily shaken.

"Well," she said, cautiously granting me this one quirk, "if there's no hot cereal to suit you, we'll allow you the carbohydrate credits elsewhere in the meal. How about bread? Do you like bread?"

"Yes." She was writing it down. "With butter and jelly," I added. "But I suppose I'm not allowed jelly anymore."

"Jelly? Oh no, Miss Goldstein. There's no jelly in a diabetic's diet. Jelly is on the list of foods which must be entirely avoided. It's in the same category as sugar, candy, honey, jams, marmalade." She seemed to be reading something off in her mind. "Syrups, pie, cake, cookies, pastries, soft drinks, candy-coated gum." She certainly was warming up to it. Until now, her voice had been low, well-modulated, pleasant. But now it was beginning to sound loud, raucous, you might even say. She wasn't finished, either. But we were approaching some kind of cadence.

"Fried, scalloped, or creamed foods, beer, wine, or other alcoholic beverages. And you must eat only the foods on your diet list. And you must eat only the amounts of food on your diet list. And you must never eat anything which is not on your diet list like candy, sugar, honey, jams, marmalade, syrups, pie . . ." She was off again. All my favorites.

"Where *is* my diet list?" I asked. "I haven't seen one." I could hardly wait. Was there any food that she didn't name on her "Eat It and You Die" list? No wonder they didn't give me a diet sheet. It would be a blank piece of paper.

"I'm surprised that you don't know about your diet. But we certainly can't blame you for that if no one's given you the booklets," she said, reaching into a manila envelope which she had carried with her. She took out a whole lot of printed stuff and passed it to me piece by piece. The first one was called "Diabetic's Diet Planner—Your Guide To Varied and Satisfying Meals." It was suspiciously thin. As I accepted it, the book fell open to a page which read:

MEAT EXCHANGES
Protein   7 Gm.   Fat   5 Gm.   Calories 73 (30 Gm. equal 1 oz.)

Since it looked like anyone who followed this book's advice would end up hungry, I asked my fortune genie, "Are hamburgers with ketchup and relish on there?" And the yellow-bellied thing answered ASK AGAIN LATER.

Miss Jew asked me if I liked every available food in the world, except of course, things like sugar, candy, honey, jams, marmalade, and alcoholic beverages. Every time I said anything, she wrote it down. Sometimes I didn't even know anymore whether I liked the thing or not, so I just answered, "Yes, yes, no," in that order.

"Papaya?"

"Yes."

"Okra?"

"Yes."

"Greens like beet, chard, collard, dandelion, kale, mustard?"

"No."

When she finally left, she promised to send me a diet which she would prepare personally from her lists of all likes and dislikes. It would be mine to take home with me. That was encouraging. At least she seemed sure that someday I would be going home. She also promised that these same foods would appear on my hospital trays, beginning, oh happy day, with my dinner tonight.

Mother and I, both weary from our evaluation of every known edible, discussed Miss Jew and her dietary edicts with a desperate resignation.

"I wonder if she is Jewish," said Mother, more to herself than to me.

"I don't think Chinese people are."

"There must be some Chinese Jews. An odd sect or something," Mother persisted.

"I'll bet Linda Christian is Christian," I offered. Mother ignored it.

"How would I know how many grams in a serving of food," she mused, "unless I weighed it? Do you think she means I have to weigh everything? Every helping of food? It seems impossible. After a while, you must get so that you can judge."

"Maybe you could teach Tessie." Our maid.

"Never," she said. "Let me look at that diet book."

I passed the thin book to Mother and leafed through some of the other propaganda about diabetes which the dietician had left. The largest booklet was called "A Guide for the Diabetic." It was filled with charts showing pictures of how it all works in the nondiabetic but doesn't work at all in the diabetic. There were hypodermic syringes, needles, and bottles of insulin, as if I needed to see pictures of *them*. The insulins had strange, odd names and different-colored labels like Regular, NPH, PZI, and Lente.

A certain paragraph stood out from the others.

Many famous people have lived long, full, and
productive lives despite diabetes. A few ex-
amples are novelist Hugh Walpole; writer-
historian H. G. Wells; statesman Georges
Clemenceau; artist Paul Cézanne; composer
Giacomo Puccini; athletes Billy Talbert and
Ham Richardson; and New York's mayor,
Fiorello H. LaGuardia.

Wow. It was quite a list if you didn't count the fact that most of
them were dead.

"What's that?" Mother asked, looking up from her diet book.

"Something for my wallet," I answered, thinking of the bulging
picture folder which I carried with my money. This new one
really would be a sensation. A little bit scary, maybe. But everybody would notice it.

"Let me see," said Mother, reaching out. I handed the card to
her. In large letters, it read:

I AM A DIABETIC
I AM NOT INTOXICATED

If I am unconscious or my behavior is peculiar,
I may be having a reaction associated with
diabetes or its treatment.

EMERGENCY TREATMENT

If I am able to swallow, give me sugar in some
form—candy, syrup, cola or similar beverages
that contain sugar, orange juice etc.—and call
a doctor or emergency hospital.

In the empty space on one side, there was a big red cross with an
evil-looking snake wound around a stick in the middle. The card
would definitely do a snow job when someone bored in Math
would say, "Let me see your wallet."

Mother was also snowed, but in the opposite direction. She
looked like she'd just seen the ghost of her mother's mother, may
she rest in peace.

"Intoxicated. Indeed," she exclaimed in anger. "You'll not carry
this card, Jane. Understand that."

"Some kids my age drink," I answered. "You read about it all
the time in the papers." It was a dumb lie.

"Mind what you say to me," she warned. "Children of your age do not drink. And you will not carry this card. Not under any circumstances. It would be like wearing a sign on your back that you have diabetes. I've already told you, it's none of anyone's business. You're not to tell a single person. If anyone asks you why you're not eating the ice cream and cake, then you can say that it's because you're on a diet. Everyone is trying to loose weight these days. It's quite fashionable.

"But I'm so thin, Mother."

"No matter, Jane. The thinnest people I know are the ones who never touch cake or candy. How do you think they became so thin in the first place?"

"Maybe they have diabetes."

"I hope you're taking this seriously, Jane," Mother said, frowning. "Your attitude about this trouble you're having . . ." She hated to use the word "diabetes," I'd noticed it before. "Your attitude today will determine whether you live a normal, healthy life or whether you air your problems and throw yourself at the mercy of strangers. Begging for their pity like some cr . . ." She was going to say "cripple," but caught it in time. And on and on. On and on.

I too, was concerned about the card, but for reasons other than my mother. All she seemed to care about was whether or not people found out that I had diabetes. I was worried more about *having* diabetes; about getting injections all the time, and having blood drawn; about testing my urine and eating the right things; and about what it said on that card that wasn't allowed in my wallet.

If jam, jelly, honey and sweet stuff caused the dietician to have a small fit when I merely asked her if I could eat some, why would the card say "Give sugar in some form"? I mean, you either can eat sugar or you can't. It either is poison or it's not. That's what they've been telling me all these days, isn't it?

A normal person, which is what I always thought I was, can eat sugar and their body does something with it, metabolizes it, and nobody gives you a medal or anything because that's what your body is supposed to do.

Then there's a diabetic. Me. A diabetic's body is up the creek. Its pancreas, which in everybody else, produces insulin, for a diabetic produces ice in the winter. Nothing. So sugar accumulates in the blood more and more until you pass out and they rush you to the hospital and save your life. That's why I have to have all these grisly ladies digging into my veins for samples of blood all the time, and why they have to give me injections of insulin a hundred times a day, and most of all, why I'm not supposed to eat any sugar. *Ever again. Even at birthday parties.*

Then why do they say on the card, that emergency treatment for a diabetic is to give sugar? And what do they mean "*If* I am able to swallow? Why shouldn't I be able to swallow? I swallowed. Everything seemed OK so far.

I didn't know who else to consult, so I turned to my fortune-teller which was still under the covers and silently asked the question, "Am I allowed to eat sugar or not?" The answer came right up. It said SOMETIMES.

✳

"Aren't you the early bird?" asked Miss Kennedy. I was sitting in the chair next to the window, the sunlight of the new day streaming onto an open book on my lap. It was *My Antonia* by Willa Cather, a book which wasn't bad even though it was on the required reading list. I liked stories about girls who lived in great places like covered wagons which were pushing West, instead of brick apartment buildings which just stood there. Of course, now I had an added problem when I immersed myself in an adventure story such as this: where would I get my insulin? With no corner drugstores to telephone. It was something to think about. Perhaps when Father returned with a great deer for our cook-out dinner, we could first remove the deer's pancreas and squeeze me a little insulin. A nuisance, maybe, but wasn't that the way it was with the true pioneer spirit?

"Have you tested your urine, dearie?" the nurse asked.

"Yes," I replied. "A trace of sugar. Green." She nodded.

"Good. That's better than yesterday. Did you write it down?"

"Yes." I always did. It was a part of my job. "What have you got for me?" I asked the nurse.

"Come and see," she said. "A syringe and needle, all set to go, and an orange. I'd like you to practice giving the orange an injection. Would you like to try?"

"Sure," I said. "But why an orange?"

"Because we want you to get the feel of giving a shot. The way that the needle enters the skin of an orange is something like what you will feel when you inject yourself. Ready to try?"

Now I got it. They wanted me to practice on this orange and then give a real injection of insulin to myself. "I . . . I'd rather not," I said.

"You'd rather not, how are you going to learn to take your own insulin if you'd *rather* not? Who did you expect to give you your injection every day for the rest of your life?"

The rest of my life. It seemed like a long time. I didn't know. I hadn't thought much about the rest of my life. Maybe my mother. And when she died, a visiting nurse like one who came to some blind old lady in our house every morning while I waited for the school bus.

Hey. That's right. That old grandma was a diabetic and a nurse in gray had to give her an injection every day. Now I understood why. Maybe when I learn to take my own, I could stop off at the old blind lady's place and give her hers. Maybe I could find some other ladies too. In the next building and across the street. It wasn't a bad idea. I could have a regular insulin route.

"I'll try."

Without a word, Miss Kennedy snapped the orange into my left hand. Then she took the glass syringe and placed it in my right hand between the second and third fingers exactly where you'd put a pen. My thumb sat on top of the plunger ready to push it down at the right moment. She tilted my hand so that I approached the orange at an angle.

"Now," she commanded, "inject." The needle collided with the orange. For an instant there was a resistance, but then the needle pierced the soft, leathery skin and sank deep, to the end.

"Push the plunger." My thumb forced the glass barrel down.

"Now pull it straight out. In one quick motion." I pulled back. It was over.

Boy, she was happy. "You did beautifully," Miss Kennedy said, all smiles. "First try, too. I knew you would, Jane." Then her voice changed back to the old business-as-usual. "When you try it again, use less force when you go in. Your skin is softer than an orange's and the needle is very sharp. The idea is to have about half to three-quarters of the needle embedded when you push the plunger." I nodded.

"I'll be back," she said. "Meantime, you practice on that poor little orange there. I think Dr. Russell plans to teach you the real thing in a little while. And you know what happens then, don't you?"

"No. What?" I held my breath.

"Out. Home with you. Fly the coop. Once a diabetic learns how to give herself insulin and she's feeling fine, what's the use of keeping her here?" She smiled and closed the door.

I injected that orange until the needle became blunt and would hardly go in anymore. Each time I silently prayed that I would be able to do as well on myself.

✳

"Company's coming," called Miss Kennedy. She pushed the door open wide and put the stopper down. First came two student nurses, each carrying her own chair. "There," said Miss Kennedy, pointing. In unison the nurses smiled and put their chairs down, silently slipping into them. Tweedle-Dum and Tweedle-Dee. Did they rehearse? The one on the right had a piece of rubber tubing peeking out of a pocket in her stiff white pinafore, royal blue blouse underneath. It was their special uniform. What were they for? What would they do to me? They were trying to be friendly to me, to greet me with their eyes. I looked away.

Next came a third student nurse with these two kids walking on either side of her, jailer-style. They were inmates, obviously, wearing the same concentration-camp pajamas which I had also worn until Mother started bringing my own from home. There was a boy and a girl. The boy was a giant and the girl, a midget. They both wore these pale green striped robes; kind of a bleached seersucker and terry-cloth combination. The giant had the midget's robe, and the midget, the giant's. But that's what you could expect around here.

"Well. Hell-o there," said Miss Kennedy, stepping forward as if she were the hostess at some kind of great party. "Now who have we here?" she asked, putting her hand on the giant's shoulder. He looked very sulky. "Moose," he said, resenting every syllable. "Moose Archer."

"And here?" The midget. "Patty. Patty Miller."

"Moose. Patty. Meet Jane Goldstein." It was exactly like Miss Fox's Dancing Classes. Same thing, only in a hospital. We all sort of looked at each other. I don't know what she wanted us to do. Maybe kiss.

"Moose, Patty, Jane, come and sit over here." She had three chairs lined up for us. "Dr. Russell will be here in a minute or two. We're going to do an insulin injection demonstration. Why don't you three use the time to get to know each other?" She waved her hand. "Talk and all that," she said. "I'll leave you alone now." She was really gung-ho on the hostess bit. No wonder nobody ever married her. She was too creepy. "Ta-ta," she said as she left the room.

She had an interesting idea of what it was to be left alone. There were still three student nurses remaining. One for each of us if we tried anything. I wish I knew what there was to try. Then she wouldn't be disappointed.

Moose, the giant, turned to me. "Why didn't you answer?"

"I would have," I said back. "The contact disappeared."

"Who?" the midget asked.

"The contact," Moose said, annoyed. "The lady who brought the message."

"Oh." The midget remembered.

"I would have paid her, too," I said. "She just never came back for it."

"You didn't give her anything when she brought you the note?"

"Where would I get anything to give her? It's like a jail here. Bread and water."

"It's not gonna improve any, be sure of that," the midget said. She seemed to know.

"So it was you who wrote me the note?" I asked the giant, turning toward him. I could visualize the Palmer Method script as it had looked on that piece of paper. Somehow the writing sort of looked like this Moose character, here. You could imagine that he had written it.

"No," said the midget sharply. "It was me. I wrote it. I figured if you was such a rich kid that your old man didn't want you sleepin' near any poor kids, then with your money and our brains, we'd find a way to break outa here." So that was how she'd planned it. I didn't know whether I liked her or not, calling my father "my old man" and all that.

"Well, you were wrong," I told her. "I asked my father for a quarter when he came yesterday, but he said he didn't see what I would need money for in a hospital."

"You coulda told him you gotta tip on a horse," she said, disgusted.

"Anyway," said Moose, the giant. He was looking around. "It's not so hot up here. Same old cell as down where we are. Whatja get for dinner last night? Twelve grapes? Two saltines without butter?"

"Yes," I said, catching on. "And eight plain boiled lima beans with a hamburger of thirty grams measuring three by two by one-eighth. A feast for a diabetic sparrow."

"Without ketchup, mustard, or relish," Patty, the midget, added. "I guess it doesn't matter how much your old man has, it's *all* lousy in this dump." She wasn't really a midget, she was just short. Short and sort of round-looking. At first guess, you'd say she was eight, but when you heard her spouting off about this and that, you might then guess that she could be ten or so.

"How old are you, Patty?" I asked. She had big front teeth and lots of brown freckles. The student nurses who weren't supposed to be listening leaned forward in their seats. They were wondering how old she was, too.

"Nine," she said. "But I've been diabetic since I was three." The student nurses looked at each other. "What about you? How old are you?"

"Thirteen." The nurses shook their heads, whispering to each other that I wasn't.

"You look about ten to me," said Patty, somewhat withered. "How come you look ten if you're thirteen?"

I shrugged innocently. "Diabetes," I replied. Then Patty said, her tone confidential, "Moose's fifteen. He's had diabetes six months and he still hasn't learned how to give himself a shot."

"You haven't?" Moose shook his head. He seemed more angry than disgraced.

"I guess that makes me the demonstration model," Patty said proudly, adjusting her hospital bathrobe as if it were some kind of ball gown.

Dr. Russell entered the room with Miss Kennedy who was carrying a tray loaded down with shiny instruments, wads of cotton, jars of alcohol, and in the corner, a one-burner electric stove with a pot on it. Everything that happens to you in the hospital tees off with the entrance of a little tray.

"Ladies and gentlemen, cooking class is about to begin." The doctor made the grand gesture of a circus ringmaster acknowledging a tribute of brilliant trumpets, but I was the only stool pigeon who smiled. Oh yes, the nurses snickered a little bit, but Patty looked deliberately bored and Moose simply stared at the floor.

"Every morning when you get up," said Dr. Russell to the three of us, "take an ordinary pot with a strainer in it like this." He pointed to what had begun to bubble on the portable stove. "Put your syringe and needle into the strainer and allow this to boil for five minutes. This will sterilize your equipment. Do try to keep it perfectly sterile before you inject yourselves. I'll show you the best way in a minute when this is finished boiling."

"Or you'll end up like me," Patty said. Everyone looked at her. "With a big infection." Dr. Russell nodded in agreement. Then he said, more to the nurses than to us, "Diabetic children need adult supervision in the rituals that they must follow because of their disease. Our friend Patty here could use a lot more help and support in her home situation. Her present hospitalization is due to neglect of a simple technique like sterilization.

"Our other friend, Moose," he said, putting his hand on the giant's shoulder, "has just the opposite problem. Moose should be breaking out and doing some of these things for himself by now, but his diabetes has been so uncontrollable since its onset, that his parents are too frightened to encourage him to more independence in caring for himself."

"What about me?" I thought. "Which kind will I be?" I said to the doctor, "My mother doesn't let me cook at home. Unless she's right there. How can I boil everything every day, if she doesn't let me cook things?"

"Don't worry, Jane," he said. "She'll let you. As a matter of fact, she'll most likely be there to watch you and to help if you need it."

"Early in the morning, before school? Mother? I don't think she's going to like that one."

"Wrong, young lady," he said. "Your mother and I have been practicing. She's getting to be a whiz at injecting an orange and I'm quite convinced that if you were ill, or had a broken arm, and you couldn't give yourself your insulin, your mother would be able to do it perfectly well."

Fantastic. Absolutely beyond belief. My mother giving an injection. She just wasn't the type. And that was a fair statement. Anybody who ever met her would verify it. Anyone. She's a gasper, a shrieker, a fainter, the original Damsel in Distress. E-e-e-k a Mouse Girl of the Year. Sometimes you hear about people who take things in their stride. Well, not my mother. Each tiny incident of disaster in our lives becomes, for Mother, World War Three. Like the time Susan accidentally locked herself in the bathroom. Mother was standing there in the hall acting like she was in there taking pills. What I mean is, it doesn't take much to set her off.

Now I hear that this same mother of mine has not only put her manicured hands on a hypodermic syringe, but that she's actually been sticking needles in oranges, and what's more, is quite a whiz at it. Too much. And, if I ever broke my injecting arm, and my luck certainly seems to have me headed in precisely that direction, I wouldn't have to die at all. *Mother* would be able to inject me.

It was terrific. If it were only true. I'd be so proud and happy. Imagine. The old girl had really come through. If she really had.

But now I needed more than ever to learn to give it to myself. Simply imagining the fit that Mother would throw before she finally gave me a shot was nothing short of an Academy-Award-winning bad dream.

Miss Kennedy was helping Dr. Russell to assemble the three syringes, instructing as they went along: allow the water to cool, touch only the *knob* of the plunger, the *side* of the syringe, the *hub* of the needle.

"What happens if you touch another part, by accident?"

"Start again, it's no longer sterile."

The needle was to be fastened to the syringe with a slight twist after it is in place. We mustn't forget the twist, Miss Kennedy was warning.

"Or else you get a big blurp and there's the needle sticking out of you, with the insulin spilled all over the place and you have to do it again," said Patty. She knew. It sounded terrible. I hoped I would remember to give the needle that twist.

"Move the plunger back and forth until all the water is out of the syringe like this," said Dr. Russell, demonstrating. "And then place it on a flat surface to rest while you prepare the bottle of insulin. The bureau is fine."

Then he showed us how to shake the bottle, wipe its top with alcohol, and measure the dose of insulin.

"How many units are you taking today, Patty?" he asked.

"Seventy," she said, and then, looking at the student nurse who had brought her to my room, added, "I think it's seventy." The student nurse shook her head. Seventy was right.

Patty looked at the labels on two bottles of insulin and selected one of them. Deftly, she inserted the needle in the bottle, turned it upside down, and withdrew what I hoped was seventy units worth. It almost filled the entire syringe.

Everybody watched her; the nurses, Dr. Russell, Miss Kennedy, and even Moose, who up to now, had only been watching the floor. Patty placed the loaded syringe across the edge of the dresser. Accepting a piece of cotton from Miss Kennedy, she rolled up her pajama leg and wiped an area at the top of her thigh. Then she picked up the syringe and whammo, that was it. In and out. It was over before you knew it.

"Good, Patty," applauded Miss Kennedy. "But be sure to remember to wipe the site with your alcohol sponge *after* your injection as well."

Dr. Russell handed her another piece of cotton. "Patty has to be especially careful," he said to the nurses. "She's been prone to infections lately. That's why we've had her in the hospital."

The red-haired student nurse leaned forward and whispered to Patty, "That was wonderful, Patty."

The midget shrugged and said, "I once figured out when they had me lying there with nothing to do that since I was three, I've had four thousand six hundred and two injections. What's so special about this one?"

Even though she said it that way, it did seem special to me. I hoped that when it was my turn, I wouldn't freeze up or something. Old Moose, next to me, didn't seem too confident either. He was next.

"Your turn, Moose," said Dr. Russell. His lightness of tone and good cheer didn't fool anyone. Let's show Jane how it's done." Go team, go.

Moose accepted the syringe silently. He knew the order of things, you could see that. His hands were big and his movements awkward. Every so often he'd drop something, even the things which were supposed to be sterile. Or he'd bump into something. Or knock something over. It was as if his body didn't understand what he expected it to do. Or as if he hadn't known it long enough to teach his limbs how to behave. Poor guy. I wished I could call for his mother.

He tried. You could never say that he didn't. He shook, and breathed kind of funny while we all sat on the edge of our chairs watching, silently urging him on. But he couldn't do it, this poor Moose. He just couldn't. His long leg stretched out in front of him for miles, it seemed, pajamas all bunched up at the top. He held the hypodermic, the steel needle catching a beam of light now and then, poised inches away from his thigh.

But it was a frozen scene. Like when Daddy is showing movies and he stops the projector to preserve a particular frame. This was one frame which went on and on. Too long. The hypodermic was just suspended there in Moose's hand. There was no momentum. There was nothing to propel it into his alcohol-washed thigh.

Soon we all abandoned our positions of watch. Moose returned the syringe to Miss Kennedy, eyes downcast, shoulders hunched. "I can't," he whispered.

"It's all right, Moose," she said softly to him. "We'll give you your insulin downstairs later."

"Now Jane," someone said.

Now Jane. My eye fell on Dr. Russell's wristwatch. It was one of those foreign jobbies, gold with lines on it, no numbers. It was nine o'clock. On the nose. First Period was just beginning. They would be answering to the roll call now. Maybe even coming to my name at this very moment.

"Mademoiselle Goldstein?" Monsieur Jones would be asking, peering over the rims of his crazy little eyeglasses. The top half was for seeing and the bottom half for reading, or something like that.

"Elle est absente," someone would reply, John Farber, most likely. He was the self-appointed attendance officer, monitor, and so on. The worst sort. A genius. He wore the same sweater every day with an H on it, for Harvard. The trouble is, he'll end up going.

"Oui, absente," Monsieur Jones would repeat, accenting the last syllable. "When a young lady is not present, we always hear the final t. Bien, Monsieur Farber, absente." Only he pronounced Farber "Fahrbear," and his own name, which was good old-fashioned Jones, was pronounced with a continental flair which could flunk you if you didn't get it: Jon-as. Roll the J. How much I wish I were there, not here.

If wishes were horses beggars would ride. My father taught it to me. He was right. It didn't help. No matter what I wished, I would still be sitting here in this room with my thigh bare in front of all these strangers, getting ready to take my own insulin.

"How many units?" I asked.

"Forty-four. Each line represents two units." I nodded, drawing the barrel of the syringe exactly to forty-four units. The cloudy solution rushed in. Insulin. I needed this just to live. I needed it for simple things like breathing, thinking, staying alive. No frills. Nothing fancy. For the basic substance of being, I needed this gray fluid. For life. What a rotten mess.

I knew how they would be watching from the way that there wasn't a single sound in the room. Like it was some kind of free show. They were like a bunch of petrified zombies. No one moved.

Suddenly I didn't care anymore. It no longer mattered what they were doing. I had the syringe in my hand and I was ready. Somehow, as if from afar, a person wiped my leg with the cold alcohol. It was Dr. Russell. I knew that he was helping me out for now, but that this was really a part of my own job.

"*Now*," he whispered. An irresistible force began to move my arm towards my shivering thigh. I was both an observer and a participant. I watched in a dream-mirror the instant's opposition at the moment of impact when the skin was broken. It had been the same with the orange.

Then it was over. Done. Someone was taking the syringe out of my hand and I wiped my own leg with the cold cotton. They were all buzzing around me. They all knew I could do it. They knew it the minute I came out of that coma. They'd bet on me to be taking my own shots before the week was out. I would be famous. They'd shout it over the whole hospital. From the rooftops.

All except Moose. He sat while the others danced around, looking at the floor. Only once did our eyes meet.

"Do it, Moose. Do it. They'll dance for you, too," I tried to tell him silently, but he only looked away again.

And then I could think of nothing but of how it would feel to breathe in the winter air as I made my way home. Home. Home.

CHAPTER SIX

*

Sometimes I wondered why they had bothered. I mean with all the sticks and the jabs and the ambulance, shattering the peace of the quiet night.

"We're going to get you on your feet again," said the Chinese dietician, weighing my grams of lunch on a sensitive scale.

"We're going to help you out of the woods," said the nurse, clearing the path with an oral thermometer.

"We're almost out of the hot water now, Jane," said the doctor. "Almost out." The same mother taught them all how to talk. Our team is red hot. Your team is all shot.

Nobody had told me that I wouldn't like being a diabetic. They all acted like I was supposed to love it. Diabetes wasn't a rotten disease where you felt sickly and terrible for half the time, and parched and dying from thirst for the other half. It was a challenge. A new adventure. It was a test of whether I really was such a terrific kid after all. Or whether I was just pretending to be.

The answer was simple. I was just pretending. But so was my mother. And my father. And Dr. Russell. It was the way the game was played.

I had to pretend, for example, that I didn't want any soda or ice cream after school when my friends swarmed around the vendor's truck, pressing their nickels and dimes into the cracked yellow of his palm.

I would complain to my mother, "They can all have ice cream and I can't have any."

And Mother, who never ate ice cream in her life except by mistake, would say, "Don't expect to influence me by speaking of what all the others do, Jane. Our burdens are individual. Not buying ice cream and soda after school may be yours. You don't know what Judy's and Ina's and Nancy's are. You don't know because they don't discuss it with you. Naturally not. Illness is a private matter."

"I'll bet they don't discuss it because there's nothing to discuss. They don't have any burdens. Only I do."

"Utter nonsense, Jane. I assure you. And I've known human nature a good deal longer than you have, little one. Now here's a dime. Why don't you go down to the newsstand and buy yourself one of those . . . those magazines that you like so much?"

"Do you mean a comic?"

"If you'd like. Yes. Buy a comic. Now run along."

"I thought you said I wasn't allowed . . ."

"Run *along*, Jane. And nothing with violence."

Sometimes I came right out and said it. "I hate having diabetes. I hate all this stuff I have to do every morning! All the stupid things I have to remember all day long. Nobody else has diabetes. Why do I have it?"

They didn't miss a single mouthful. The shock of my bombs bursting in air didn't cause as much as a single second's delay between the soup plate and the mouth. Split pea. Homemade. They all just kept on eating.

"Now Jane, you know that's just not true. Supposing you do endure a brief inconvenience in the morning? Really, is it all that much? Once you take your insulin, you're set for the day. You're free to go ahead and lead your normal life. You get on the bus, go to classes, do your work and your play, just like all the others. Is that reason enough to have you feeling so sorry for yourself?"

"The others can eat anything they want," I tried, the match already over.

"What was it that you couldn't eat on today's menu? Name it."

"Chocolate cake," I returned gladly. "Chocolate layers with thick, chocolate icing. And for me, they brought an apple. With a wormhole at the bottom."

"And what, my dear, did *Stewie* eat when the others had their chocolate cake?" Stewie was a pest of a kid in my Form who lived in our building. Anything Stewie put into his chubby little mouth gave him these giant welts of hives. Mother was betting on a sure thing. How brave of her.

"I couldn't tell you, Mother. Stewie sits at another table, thank God."

"Thank God? You don't like Stewie?"

"I don't like him and I don't hate him. We weren't talking about Stewie to begin with."

"Well, I'll tell you what he had. He had an apple, just like you did. Stewie is not allowed to eat chocolate cake either. Now tell me, Jane. Do you suppose Stewie is making a fuss over it at his dinner table right now?"

"Having diabetes is no worse than having anything else," my father added, coming to. "You just follow a few simple rules and then you go ahead and have fun like everybody else does."

Maybe they believed it.

I began to play a little game of my own. It had to do with my daily insulin dose. Sometimes I took the amount I was supposed to take. And sometimes I took five units less. Or ten units less.

The beauty of the game was that there was no one to tell me what to do. Because no one knew. And all the rules were made up by me. If I wanted to make a new one, or break an old one, the only person I'd have to check with was myself.

Our morning ritual was as bad as something you'd dream up on Hallowe'en night. But it always ended up all right. With me safely behind the closed bathroom door giving myself exactly the amount of insulin that struck my fancy, not more, not less.

We'd start out in the kitchen, Mother and I, at about four-thirty in the morning. There we'd sit, staring at each other, much more asleep than awake, waiting for my syringe and needle to boil itself.

I'd say to Mother, "I can't see why we both have to be here while it boils. Why can't one of us do it? You? And then you can come for me when it's ready."

"No," Mother whispered, looking green-skinned under the fluorescent kitchen light. "You have to be able to do your own sterilization."

"Then why don't you go back to bed? Why do we both have to sit here? It's like a funeral."

"What's wrong with my being here too?" Mother hissed. "Can't you bear to sit for ten minutes with your own mother? I'll bet if it was one of your girl friends, you wouldn't mind."

"What are you whispering for?"

"It's still early. I don't want to awaken Tessie."

What she meant was, she didn't want Tessie to stumble out of the maid's room, look into the boiling pot and find out that I had diabetes.

Or any sleep-walking neighbors, who might just happen to be

pressing their ear against our kitchen door. Not one of them would ever find out. Because we always whispered.

The time when I could be boss over my own disease came immediately after, however. We'd stagger sleepily together, Mother and I, through the chilly halls of the apartment, bearing the newly sterilized equipment like it was the Ten Commandments coming down from Mount Sinai. I carried and Mother bodyguarded me. You didn't have to be too smart to figure out that the whole thing was crawling with contamination by the time we reached the bathroom. I never mentioned it. Because it would just mean back to the kitchen and the whole stupid thing would start again.

But once the door was closed, I was running the show. Mother would stand just outside, nervously shifting her weight, making the floor creak, listening.

"What did you get?" she'd ask, too soon.

"Nothing yet," I'd return angrily. "Can't you wait a minute?"

"You're talking to your *mother*," she warned. But she was helpless behind that closed door and we both knew it.

If only she'd go away. Leave me alone. Get off my neck for five minutes. But not Mother. She was always leaning on the bathroom door holding her breath. What did I get? What did I get?

What did she think I'd get? Negative? Three plus? One plus? The choice was limited: from negative to four plus sugar. I tested my urine twice a day, morning and evening. How could she still be so fascinated with each result? Did she think I'd get seven plus? Or maybe she hoped for a bulb that would light up at the bottom of the test tube saying "DIABETES CURED."

"Well?"

"Four plus." She made a little gasping noise.

"What did he say to do?"

"Take five more units if my urine was four plus." Every night I spoke to Dr. Russell on the telephone. I'd tell him what my urine was that day, and he'd tell me how much insulin to take the next morning.

But when I felt like playing my little game, I had to disregard his very fine advice. So sorry.

"That brings your dose to fifty-five, doesn't it? . . . Jane?"

"Yes, Mother," I answered, busily drawing forty-five units into the syringe. Now she couldn't bother me any more. No matter what she kept saying from behind the closed bathroom door.

She could say I had diabetes, or that I didn't have diabetes. Or that I was just like everybody else, or that I was just like nobody else. They were all lies and they were all true. I couldn't tell which was which anymore.

It was exciting in a way, taking my own injection. Naturally, I hate injections. But taking my own insulin was different.

"It's a big responsibility," they said to me. "It's crucial that you do it correctly." They used their serious, charcoal-gray, "Let's level" voices to tell it to me, so that I'd get the picture.

But they were wrong. That's what I found out when I started playing my little game. It wasn't so crucial that I do it precisely right. Almost every day I was taking doses which varied from five to ten units from what had been ordered. And I was still alive. I began to wonder if I really did have diabetes in the first place.

"Jane? Did you take it? Did you give it to yourself yet?"

"No, Mother . . . almost . . . there." I snapped open the bathroom door. It was the signal that I had finished. She leaped upon me, her eyes fearfully darting here and there for evidence of some trouble.

"Is it all right? Did it bleed?"

"No, Mother. Everything's fine," I answered evenly. She sighed, a great, windy heave.

"Thank God," she said, under her breath.

To cheer her, I said, "Will you tell Daddy that it's all OK? That I did it, the test and the shot?" We had been reporting this information in regular bulletins.

"Your father's asleep," Mother replied with great disdain. Then she adjusted her bathrobe and started away, saying, "Get dressed. I'll see about breakfast."

I knew that she was angry with my father. Not just because he was still asleep; it was hardly daybreak, even now. It was because he could be asleep and Mother couldn't. Because she would have liked to have divided the worry, the jitters and the general job of Jane Goldstein, Child Diabetic. And for some reason, the world is set up so that the mother gets most of it.

I went into their darkened bedroom where my father was sleeping. I whispered loudly, "Daddy, I did it. It all worked out fine. I took the shot, Daddy."

"Huh?" He raised his head, squinting at me through sleepy, swollen eyelids. "Jane? You did it? You did it, you say?" It was like talking to an interplanetary person, but I thought I should tell him.

"Yes, Daddy. The insulin shot. I did it."

"You did it, huh? Wonderful, baby. That's my girl."

"You're glad?" Mother was right. Deep down, the worry was not his.

"Glad? I sure am, honey. Someday you'll show me how you do it. OK?"

"Sure, Daddy. Someday." That's all I needed. The TWO of them hanging around there in the hallway.

✳

The telephone rang. We were sitting quietly, Mother knitting something which required her to constantly count things to herself. Her lips were moving like the little bearded man in the synagogue whose job it was to pray for everybody, all the time. Even everybody who was dead. It was quite a job if you think about it. Not leaving anybody out, I mean.

Tessie came to the door. "For you, Mrs. Goldstein. It's Miss Marks, the nurse at the Gate School." Tessie answered the telephone, even when we were all right there next to it, and she was up to her elbows in pie dough in the kitchen. It was to screen out I don't know what.

Mother suddenly became very tense again, bolting up to her feet and allowing her precious knits and purls to slip off her lap.

"I'll take it inside," she said to no one, but I suppose, to me. And then she was off, running softly on the carpeted floors towards the privacy of her own bedroom.

It's true that taking the wrong amount of insulin every day was making me sometimes sick and sometimes irritable, but it certainly seemed that Mother didn't have to rush off like that to her bedroom when there was a telephone right here on the library desk. As a punishment for her lack of courtesy. I slipped the receiver off the hook.

"Mrs. Goldstein?" the nurse's voice was saying. "Miss Marks, returning your call."

"I wanted to speak to you about my daughter Jane, Miss Marks. She's in the First Form, Miss Lucky's section."

"Yes," the nurse replied. "I know which one she is." The week before I got diabetes, she had fixed up a cut on my knee. Miss Marks wasn't so bad if you liked nurses. She was about sixty-two or so and fat in a nice way, with a gentle, calm voice which made you believe that she might be for real. "I'm glad to see that her name is off the absentee list," Miss Marks said to my mother. "It must have been a fright for you to have her hospitalized with pneumonia."

"That's why I'm calling, Miss Marks," Mother said. "It wasn't pneumonia."

"*Not* pneumonia, Mrs. Goldstein? I was quite sure that the list said . . ." She spoke calmly.

"We sent word to her teacher that she was ill with pneumonia," Mother said, drawing her breath in with a little gasp, "but what she actually had . . . has," she corrected herself quickly, "is . . . diabetes."

"Diabetes!" Miss Marks exclaimed. "Why, that's quite different, isn't it?" There was a minute when nobody said anything. When Miss Marks got used to the switch, she said, "Is she taking insulin?"

"Fifty-five units of protomine zinc."

"In one shot?"

"Yes. In the morning before she comes to school."

"Does someone come in to give it to her?"

"No," Mother said. "She's taking it herself. They taught her how in the hospital and she seems to be doing all right with it."

"Good for her," Miss Marks said, and you could tell that she meant it. "That's a brave little girl, Mrs. Goldstein. We'll certainly cooperate fully here at school to make her routines as easy as we can. Were any restrictions placed on her activity?"

"None that I know of," Mother said. "Her doctor is Dr. Frederick Russell. He's a specialist in diabetes. I believe he said he would call you." Mother paused. "There's one other thing, Miss Marks. We, Mr. Goldstein and I, want *no one* to know that Jane is a diabetic. No one. What I'm telling you now is in the strictest professional confidence. We were advised that the school must be told with an illness as unpredictable as diabetes."

"Yes," Miss Marks said. "I would think so."

"That's what I'm doing right now, Miss Marks," said Mother in a dark and serious voice. "Telling the school."

"I see," said the nurse. And I'll bet she did.

"We have instructed Jane that she is to discuss her illness with none of her friends and none of her teachers. She would have no reason for doing so. Mr. Goldstein and I believe firmly, Miss

Marks, that one's state of health is a private matter and that Jane will lead a fuller life if others assume that she is perfectly normal. She is a wonderful child. Artistic, mathematically inclined, graceful, happy-go-lucky. She'll learn to take this in her stride." Mother meant that I'd better learn.

"I don't approve of this, Mrs. Goldstein," Miss Marks said firmly, but still in her quiet voice. "Jane has developed an illness which will be with her for the rest of her life. By swearing her to secrecy, you will force her to play a role, the nondiabetic, when she's out in the world. Yet in reality, she must be expected to follow strictly the rules of her disease in order to live. You're counting on the fact that diabetes is an invisible illness. But Jane's two roles will overlap. They have to. And when that happens, Mrs. Goldstein, there'll be trouble.

"What will happen, for example," she continued, hammering, "when Jane feels fatigued by activities that do not tire the other children? Do you realize that your attitude will prevent her from slowing down to rest? And what, Mrs. Goldstein, when Jane needs an extra meal at an odd hour, as diabetics often do? What if she becomes hypoglycemic, if she has an insulin shock?"

"She's going to carry candy with her at all times, Miss Marks," my mother returned. "A roll of Lifesavers in her purse. Then if she feels the effects of too much insulin, she can eat the candy. Lots of children suck candies, you know." There was a pause at Miss Marks' end.

Softly, she said, "Her teachers should know, Mrs. Goldstein."

"All of them?" Mother continued, arguing. "Every one who sees Jane for an hour a week? Her shop teacher? Her ceramics teacher? The man who shows her how to feed paper into a printing press? You believe that they all need to know that Jane has diabetes? No, Miss Marks. If you please, none of them. And if the need to tell specific individuals ever arrives, we can decide at that time."

"I cannot promise that, Mrs. Goldstein. But we will certainly give full consideration to your wishes. The headmaster and I will discuss it and try to keep your point of view in mind."

"Thank you, Miss Marks," Mother said crisply. "Please do."

✻

In gym I asked if I could sit down. We were having stunts, this thing where they put mattresses down on the floor and then they tell you different ways of piling up so that you made something, a pyramid or a flying angel or some crazy balancing thing like that. I asked the teacher, "Jeff, is it all right if I sit down for a few minutes?" and she said, "Sure, Jane. Sit over there so you don't get kicked."

Gym was the only place where you could be that informal with the teachers. Jeff's name was Miss Jefferson. But all the other gym teachers seemed to have nicknames too, even if they were forty-two or so. One teacher's name was Mendy; the one who taught swimming was good old-fashioned Sherm; and the head of the gym department was another lady with a man's name. Georgie. But you didn't get to call her that unless you became a captain.

I sat down because I didn't feel right. Sort of restless. It wasn't anything you could point to, the way you could with a pain in your stomach. I was jumpy. The shouts of the other people seemed louder than usual and I wanted to get away from them. Things looked sharper than they should. It was uncomfortable; they were too sharp. Details of what was in front of me competed for my attention. Colors, shapes, voices, each one was separate. Nothing belonged.

But that was all. Things just didn't look exactly right. Or feel exactly right. But it wasn't all that wrong, either. Which was why I didn't ask to go to the nurse or anything. Besides, I had one more class today. Music.

The school made us have music every day because Plato told them to. Same for arithmetic. And if Plato had told them to go blow up the Brooklyn Bridge, they would have been there with the dynamite long ago. This idol worship was especially bad for me because I hated music and I hated arithmetic. And what I thought about Plato and his opinions . . . oh, well.

I arrived at music late because I couldn't find one of my socks. I ended up wearing one gym sock and one regular sock which they asked you not to do because they didn't like the gym smells to escape from the gym building, where they loved them. I didn't feel any better and I didn't feel any worse. I just felt funny.

Old Cottheim had a record going of the Rhine maidens flying around. He sat in his usual pose, shiny bald head lowered, cradled in his hands, staring hard at the floor. His trance, we were all supposed to think but nobody did, was because of the beautiful music.

"Sign a late slip, Goldstein," he said without ever looking up. Bad news. Fourth late slip. It meant a detention. I was better off absent.

I made out the late slip and wrote in the blank space at the bottom COULDN'T FIND MY OTHER SOCK, which I'm sure will touch the heart of the lady who types up the detention list. Then I crawled into my seat which was in the last row because old Cottheim seated you according to how musical you were.

I was getting rapidly worse. I was glad to be able to sit down. My knees felt weak, as if at any moment they would have given way, sending me tumbling forward. But sitting down didn't make things any better. A certain shaking feeling was beginning in my hands. A rumbling. If I wanted to do something now, reach out and pick up, or button a button, or bring a spoon from a plate to my mouth, I wonder if I could.

No one seemed to notice anything. Even Judy and Ina, who sat on either side of me pretending to be in another world from the music, maybe were in another world. I looked down at my clasped hands on the wooden desk. They were still. The trembling was from within. What was wrong with me? Maybe something to do with diabetes. But a thing I'd never had before. Maybe I was coming down with some kind of rare shaking disease. That would be my rate of speed. Always room for one more.

Old Cottheim had switched over to the Incidental Music from *A Midsummer Night's Dream*. It was some terrifice idea that Plato had of coordinating the English and the music plans. We were supposed to join in as Titania sang to all the woodsie people named Cobweb, Moth, Mustardseed and guys like that. A sing-along, brilliant lyrics by William Shakespeare. My classmates' rotten voices grated:

So. So good night. So good night. (Repeat fourteen times.)

I tried to open my mouth to sort of sing along because old Cottheim was very particular about that, but nothing happened. My voice wasn't there. My neck and chest were covered with a cold, clammy sweat. Inside my body there was an alarm sounding. A hot, red gong was ringing and there was pushing and panic.

Insulin shock. Of course. That's what it had to be. Too much insulin. I had taken extra units today, just to see what would happen. Dr. Russell had told me to watch out for a shock. If I felt weak . . . if I felt shaky . . . take some candy, he'd said. I'd feel better the minute I got some sugar into me. I had to carry it with me at all times.

I reached for the leather purse which contained the two nickel rolls of doughnut-shaped hard candies. I had been carrying these very ones since my diabetes trouble began. One roll of red and one assorted. If only I could get to them.

My fingers were thick and clumsy. It was as if they were webbed together like a duck's. They didn't seem to work separately any more. My hand shook openly now. I fumbled with the zipper of my purse. Such an easy thing, pulling open a zipper. Just grab the pulley and one, two, three. Again and again it slipped out of my useless fingers. All around me they sang: "So good night. Good n-i-g-h-t, Sweet dreams."

A thin black veil, a curtain of gauze was lowered and then raised before my eyes. I strained against the black tint, widening my eyelids, stretching them open to their fullest. Now I had my hand on one of the rolls of hard candy. I let it fall onto my lap. There was something to pull, a paper string, in order to get the first one out. My hands weren't working right, they trembled and shook. If only my fingers would respond properly for the one minute I needed to rip at the paper.

"What's with you?" Judy whispered over the tremolo of dancing fairies.

"Nothing." I looked at her through the black haze. A round rock of a candy fell free onto my lap. Part of its surface was smashed. The fragments, like shattered glass, clung to my woolen skirt. I scooped up what I could catch and put it into my mouth, brutally grinding down with my molars. "Eat as many as you need," Dr. Russell had told me. "Stop when you feel better." I ate another one and then another.

"Hey," said Ina, holding out her hand under the desk. "Me, too."

"Yeah. And me," said Joycie, stretching her arm across Ina's lap. Soon they were all asking for one in gestures or whispers or wild signals which flew from one row to another.

"Pass one down," called Michael from across the center aisle. I put another candy into my own mouth. The black veil had disappeared.

Suddenly the room was quiet. They were all looking at me. The turntable was still and all the singing and forest merrymaking had stopped.

"You're being a real wise guy today, Goldstein, aren't you?" The silence dared you. Nobody moved. I looked down at my clasped hands. They weren't trembling so badly any more. The sugar was beginning to work against the overdose of insulin. Thank God.

"I'm sorry, sir," my lips moved without a single sound.

"Passing out candy as if you were at the circus? I'll tell you what kind of circus you're at, young lady," he said, tapping his finger, a thumping metronome, against the hollow side of the spinet piano. "A *one ring* circus." Thump, thump, thump. "With the ring-leader . . . right . . . here." Somewhere a pencil fell to the wooden floor. "Now you are excused, Miss Goldstein. Sit in my office across the hall. I'll see you after class."

Would my legs carry me, ablaze with humiliation, across the room and into the dark safety of the hallway? The worst of my symptoms had gone. I could walk, a little wobbly, but without attracting any further attention.

I sank into the chair near his desk, waiting. I ate what was left of the candies; a lime one, an orange, another lime, one that was cherry red. It was true. The sugar was making me better. I felt tired, as if after a great physical exertion. But I was myself again. The shock was over. The sharpness was gone. The shakiness. Would this happen to me again? Without warning? What if it happened tomorrow while I was in the swimming pool? Where does a diabetic keep her candy while she is swimming?

And what would happen to me now when old Cottheim comes and starts bawling me out for eating candies in music? Everywhere I looked there was trouble. Even the fresh kids didn't fool around with old Cottheim. This was the first time I'd ever been thrown out of anybody's class. Maybe I'd have to tell him that I was eating candy because I was having an insulin shock. The truth. The best way, my father used to say. But he hasn't said it lately.

He came into his office and looked through some mail on his desk. He knew I was there all along, but he wanted to show me how unimportant I was. I got it. Finally, he removed a large white handkerchief from his pocket and blew his nose.

"Well, Goldstein," he said sternly, "what have you got to say for yourself?"

"I'm sorry I was eating in class, sir," I whispered, wishing it would end there.

"Not good enough," he snapped. "You'd better say something else in your own defense. And make it good." OK, old Cottheim, you asked for it.

"I was eating the candy, sir, because I have diabetes and I needed the sugar." His eyes looked into mine and held on. He said nothing. He simply kept gripping me with his vise of a gaze, cool and green. He was deciding.

Then he picked up the receiver of the telephone on his desk and dialed three digits, still keeping his eyes on mine for the whole time. If you're bluffing, sister, you're finished. The two flecked marbles penetrated, slicing at my insides.

"Miss Marks?" he said into the telephone, watching me. Why was I afraid? What I told him was true, wasn't it? "I have a First Former here named Jane Goldstein. Jane Goldstein says . . . she was eating candy in class because she has . . . diabetes." He stopped and listened. Now he turned off his eyes for a moment. Closed them. His face changed and changed again.

"Don't you think I could have been informed, Miss Marks? I see this child for forty minutes every day. Shouldn't there be some communication between you in the administration building and those of us who teach the children? This seems to me to be just another example . . ."

Miss Marks interrupted and old Cottheim listened again. Was she explaining that when my mother demanded that a secret be kept, no one dared to go against her?

Old Cottheim shook his head hopelessly. "Look, Miss Marks, I've got the kid sitting here in my office. Let me discuss it with you personally at another time." Then he turned to me and said, "Miss Marks wants to know if you need her." I shook my head.

"No," I said to old Cottheim. "Tell her it's over."

"If you ever need to eat anything in my class, Jane, you go right ahead," he said after he hung up. "Anytime at all. You have my personal permission." He looked awfully worried. I almost wished I didn't hate music.

"Don't worry, old Cottheim," I thought. "I won't hold it against you."

"Thank you, Mr. Cottheim. Thank you," I said, making little shuffling rise-and-shine motions in my chair so that he'd get the idea that I had to make the bus in a few minutes.

"Now you run along. And don't forget to eat if you have to." I nodded, scooping up my books. "I'm tearing up this late slip, too," he added, doing it with a loud rip.

On the bus ride home, I dozed in fits, waking with a jolt to the gasp of the air brakes as we twisted through traffic.

"So good night," sang Queen Titania in an eerie, witch voice. And the fairies fled on fields of panic.

CHAPTER SEVEN

You could always find a little guerrilla action at our dinner table. Our sacred, holy dinner table. Where they all ate pheasant under glass while I got fourteen grams of grated gravel. Spring had come and now I was twelve. For all the good that it did me.

It was Friday night, time for the Sabbath meal to begin. My parents were ordinary religious fanatics. They could have been Holy Rollers, but they happened to be Jews.

Mother began the ceremonies with the lighting of the Sabbath candles. It was something I once enjoyed, the welcoming of the Sabbath Queen. The beautiful table, the crisply ironed napkins, the crystal glasses which shot off rainbow balls when the overhead light shined on them.

But these days Mother was upstaging the Sabbath Queen. And I was trapped for the performance. Matches in hand, Mother stood waiting like the headmaster for our undivided attention. Then she would light the candles, holding up her hands in blessing. So far, bearable.

But then it began. The seance. She'd close her eyes and throw herself into this private fit. She was trying to radio either God or the Sabbath Queen. I never found out which.

Yes, yes, it was so, God. She'd nod her head in resignation, tears streaming out from under her closed eyelids. Mother could take her punishment. Yes sir, God, Mother would have to take what she got. If there was anything that she knew, she knew that.

What was it that she got? Me. Naturally. You really couldn't mistake it. Sometimes she'd had enough of my father. And once in a while, she'd reach her limit with that brat of a sister. But without a doubt, the payoff was me, the Diabetic Quiz Kid. Maybe she wasn't perfect herself, she was telling the Sabbath Queen, but with all her soul-searching, she couldn't figure out what she'd done to deserve me.

The Sabbath Queen didn't say anything much. So after awhile, she gave up on the prayer routine and came around the table on her kissing route, saying "*Gut Shabbos.*" When she got to me, I whispered directly into her ear, "Why didn't you send in my consent slip for Valley Farm? I'm the only one in the form who didn't get it in."

Clearly, that was fresh, nonreligious, inappropriate and rude. Trembling, Mother said, "Your *father* is making the Kiddish."

Now we all turned towards Daddy, who held the special wine cup high in his right hand as he sang the sweet melody. A finger followed the words in his stained prayer book even though he knew them by heart. I didn't mind watching my father. He read what was in the book without any sniffing or weeping. You came to appreciate that.

Mother had started some new crying back at her end of the table. She'd look at Daddy and then at me and then at Susan, taking it all in, engraving the happy family scene on her mind to remember forever. Who knew if next week we'd all be alive?

I waited until we sang "Amen" and then I said, "Why didn't you send in my consent slip for Valley Farm?"

"It's Friday night," Mother said. "Must we discuss it at the dinner table?"

"Yes, we must," I said clearly. So she tried my father.

"Abe, are you going to sit there and let her disrupt our meal?" Our sacred, blessed, heavenly meal.

"No fighting, girls," my father advised between spoonfuls of chicken soup.

"I'm not trying to fight, Daddy," I said. "I just want to know when Mother is going to send in my consent slip for the Valley Farm trip. It's next weekend and I'm the only one in the form whose slip isn't in yet. Mr. Winthrop said that if it's not signed and in his office by Monday morning, I can't go."

"Tell Mr. Winthrop that you're not going," said my mother, just like that. "You have family obligations."

"What do you mean?"

"I mean that next Sunday is Shevuoth, a very important Jewish holiday. You have to be in the synagogue with your family instead of running around in dungarees with your friends on some horse farm."

She couldn't be serious. She just couldn't. The Valley Farm trip

was the highlight of the First Form year. It was a landmark, a
school tradition, like Founder's Day. In every senior yearbook,
there was a whole page devoted to the snapshots taken when the
graduates were First Formers like me, at their Valley Farm trip.

No one had ever said I couldn't go before this. Mother had been
to all the briefing meetings where they explained about how there
would be fifteen adult chaperones for every child. It made no
sense.

"Do I have to go to schul, too?" asked Susan.

"Of course," Mother replied. "We'll all go. Together. Eat your
salad, Jane. The dressing has your fat allowance for today on it."

"No. I'm not eating another mouthful. I'd like to be excused."

"Nonsense. You're not finished. You're not allowed to skip
dinner, Jane. You'll have an insulin shock."

Simple, Jane. You're not allowed to skip your dinner. The rule.
It was like death and taxes. If you're not allowed to skip your
dinner, then you'd just better open your mouth and eat. Well,
sorry, everyone. There's been a little change in plans.

"I'll never eat again until we settle this thing about my overnight
at Valley Farm."

"If you get to go, don't exepct to borrow my pink sweater,"
Susan put in.

"Butt out," I snapped.

"Do you know that you're talking to your own family? To
your mother? And to your sister?"

"I don't care who you are. I'm not staying home because of some
Jewish holiday that nobody ever paid any attention to before.
You're just pretending that we're religious because you don't want
me to go."

Mother got up and shut the swinging door to the kitchen so that
the maid wouldn't hear us fighting and find out that I have
diabetes.

"On a Friday night," she said to my father, shaking her head in
misery, "you allow this child to disrupt our home on a Friday
night?" The way she said it. Our home. On a *Friday* night.

"Jane. Eat your dinner. Don't threaten us. Let's talk about it."

"All right, Daddy. Talk," I said, not touching my fork. "No one
ever told me, when they announced the Valley Farm trip, that I
couldn't go because it was a Jewish holiday. Why do you suddenly
decide now? It's not fair."

"We don't check our calendar that far in advance," said my mother.

"No, Mother. You're not letting me go to Valley Farm because you're afraid that my friends will find out that I have diabetes. I know it when you're trying to make up an excuse."

"You're calling your own mother a liar?" She was beginning to cry. It was a terrible trouble that I was in. I didn't want to call Mother a liar, but I had to go to Valley Farm.

"Maybe we could arrange a way," my father suggested. "A way for Jane to manage to take her insulin without anyone knowing. Dr. Russell is very much in favor of her going, you know," he said to my mother.

"*He's* in favor," my mother returned smartly, "what does he have to loose if something goes wrong?"

"Why can't she get up earlier than the others, go off to the bathroom, take the shot, and crawl back into bed? Nobody would be the wiser." Maybe the tide was turning. Daddy seemed for it.

"I went to the meeting specifically to hear the sleeping quarters being described," Mother said. "The girls will sleep in the main house, dormitory style. There could be ten to twelve other girls in the same room with her. Someone will discover."

"Yes," said Susan. "And then what?"

It really was the Question of the Year, but I just said to her, "Shut up, Susan. Keep out of it." Daddy was dangerously thoughtful.

"I can see how you'd manage to take your shot in private, Jane," he said. "But how could you do all the rest? Test your urine, boil the syringe?" I was ready for that one.

"The doctor said I could prepare a sterile setup using a metal container filled with alchohol for the syringe and needle. He even said that for one day I could skip testing my urine. No boiling and no testing. Can you imagine what a holiday it would be?"

No one spoke. It was up to Mother.

"And what," she blurted, breaking the silence with her suddenness, "what if she doesn't feel well during the day? What if she has a shock? They're planning to use the children to get the farm ready for the summer campers. There'll be plenty of physical exertion, painting, building, cleaning, God knows what they'll have them doing. Supposing it's too much for her?"

"Let her keep a few packs of those candies she carries in her pocket. Just like she does now. Same thing. Get her dungarees with pockets, can't you?"

Now was the time to beg. The crucial moment. The turning point. I shuddered at how degrading it was, how unfair to me. If I didn't have diabetes, there would be nothing to struggle over. The other kids . . . the ones who had no diseases, their mothers and fathers simply signed the consent slip without a word. Just took out their little pens and wrote their names.

"May I? I'll be careful. Nothing will happen. I promise. Nobody will find out." It was my closing speech to the jury. My summation. I was as close to convincing her as I would ever be. If Mother refused now, I would not be able to go. It was that simple.

She looked at me for a long time. Like she maybe expected the Voice of the Lord. If only I were a ventriloquist, I'd have given her heaven's word for it. With angels singing in the background.

I waited.

"All right," she then said softly. "Jane will go."

❊

I took the right amount of insulin on the day that we left for Valley Farm. It was a private gesture of appreciation to my parents because they had decided to let me go. It was also because I hoped that everything would come off without a hitch. I wanted to be able to do what they had been telling me was so easy; just take my insulin and forget that there was such a thing as diabetes. After that, be exactly like everyone else. No shocks, no comas, no disease, just feeling like a good, old-fashioned healthy stool pigeon.

The nearest hospital was seven miles away; there was no ambulance service. The roads were paved but not lighted. It was an accredited institution and they'd heard of diabetes. Mother had checked it all out just in case.

Certain teachers who had the lower forms in their classes came with us on the trip. There was a great excitement when they announced which teachers were going. We could imagine what fun it would be when we ate at the same tables, played on the same teams, slept in the same rooms.

Jonesy the French teacher always came. In the summer he was the director of a camp in the mountains. This was right up his alley. And there was the old battle-axe, McCormack, who taught something called Remedial Reading, but not to me, thank goodness. And Mrs. de Paredes, old Cottheim, and, attention everybody, Miss Marks, the nurse.

Not that she followed me around. That much I'll say for her. But how she came to be at Valley Farm when in her whole life she'd never been out of the nurse's office, I could guess had to do with me. Just in case.

There was no valley and there was no farm, but it still looked beautiful to me. It lay on the gentle shore of a great violet lake, a small campsite cut out of a wild jungle of birchbark, and thorns, and spiceberries, and wild flowers. Valley Farm was something called a charity camp. That means that the children who come are partly poor and partly sick and partly both. They only got to stay for two weeks out of the summer, instead of eight weeks like it is at my camp.

Correction. My former camp. I wasn't going anymore, I'd been told. I was getting too old for camp. Too mature for all that kiddy stuff. My sister was still of the right age, of course. But then she didn't have diabetes.

"There *is* a camp for me," I had excitedly reported one day after a visit to Dr. Russell. It's called Camp Nyda. Right here in New York state. The name means New York Diabetic Association. Nyda. See? They *like* having diabetics. They're not afraid if the children have shocks. That's what they're for."

"Down an eighth," said my father, adding up what happened to his stocks today. I was still in there trying even though I knew that they weren't going to let me go to any Camp Nyda. A diabetic camp? What would they tell Aunt Bertha? That I was the camp nurse?

"No," said my father. "That's a camp for diabetic poor kids. It's a charity camp. You're diabetic, but you're not poor. So you wouldn't fit in too well. Come with us this summer, with Mother and me. We'll see the United States, stay at a nice hotel here and there, swim in the Pacific Ocean. Travel a little." He whacked my behind. "That's better than some diabetic charity camp, isn't it?"

That's how I knew about a charity camp. I was sick, but I wasn't poor.

At Valley Farm, we painted a fence. We were kids who were born in the city. Not one of us had ever held a paintbrush outside of art class. Not one of us had even been allowed to watch when the painters came into our apartments with their scaffolds, carefully spreading a cover over the inlaid wooden floors. "Out, out," we were whisked. "It's not good to breathe that stuff."

At Valley Farm we breathed. And we didn't need lessons with a broad-base brush, either. We knew what to do as we soaked the blanched, even logs with redwood stain. Proudly, we allowed it to spill all over our work clothes and sneakers. It was our medal of honor. For hard work.

But I was uneasy. A predinner softball game had been started. The diamond had been weeded and swept clean by a group of my classmates earlier that afternoon. It was boys against girls. The teachers were playing. The girls could have used me. But I was worried that if I played, my blood sugar would fall too low and I would have an insulin shock. So I sat under a tree with a certain group of drips who never participate in anything and talked to them, all the while pulling long, fat weeds out of the grass and crushing their juicy green stems between my teeth.

I was worrying myself right out of a good time. And I knew it. But knowing it didn't help. How dumb it was, how idiotic, to fight so hard to get here and then to find that I could think of nothing besides the danger of discovery which lurked differently within each endless hour. It hammered in my head. It had taken me over.

The burden was the pact with my parents. They had let me come. I had to keep the secret. If anyone found out that I had diabetes, it would mean that I had broken the pact. My job was to prevent it. It was like having two diseases. One was diabetes. The other was Keeping the Secret. Either way, it was lousy. And I was having a terrible time.

Everyone was waiting for the evening activity. It was a square dance. With old Cottheim as caller. I wore my new pair of dungarees, boy's, with a fly front. The back pocket held my roll of Lifesavers. In case I dosie-doed too hard and got an insulin shock. The bulge finished my figure.

"Hey, look," Mr. McCormack teased, "Goldstein's got roses in her cheeks."

"I don't know," old Cottheim answered, detaining me by putting a hand on my shoulder. "Maybe it's rouge. We don't allow First Formers to wear make-up, do we, Mr. McCormack?" Judy, Ina and Nancy stood around giggling.

"Nope. Not until Third Form. And then only lipstick. What shall we do with her?"

"Decide after you have a look at her buddies over there. And the rest of them. Over there. And there." They looked from one group to the other. We all had flaming red cheeks, boys and girls alike.

"Guess we'd better let 'em all off this once," Mr. McCormack shrugged, as we scattered, shrieking with the joy of liberation.

With them, it was very romantic; a sonnet, a love song. It was the effect of a day in the sun, the sport of following a bee along the easy slope of a green meadow, the anticipation of the dancing to come. But with me, it was strictly the fear of getting caught.

I worried that Daphne Wladecki had gone through my things. I don't know why it was Daphne in particular, but I just had this feeling about her. She'd taken the bed across the aisle from mine. And she was watching me when I got dressed. Why? Was I so rare? Then I left because I was finished first, and she stayed behind, still dressing. I worried that when I went, she opened my suitcase and saw my syringe and insulin. And wasn't saying anything. Yet.

I worried worse when she kept turning up in the same square with me. Something was up. We weren't friends particularly. Actually, we were more like rivals. Over Artie, who had been my partner for most of this set.

"Swing your partner round the bend" sang old Cottheim, recorded cowboys twanging their agreement. A lot of frantic violins played a sawed-off version of "Turkey in the Straw."

I watched Daphne swing her partner round the bend. She was so sure of herself, so certain about how to do the dance, so positive that her hair looked all right, that her braces weren't the kind that cut into boys' lips. Even her name. Daphne. And mine. Jane. She seemed to have everything. Even a brassiere.

"Dig for the oyster. Dig. Dive for the pearl. Now dive."

I tramped mechanically about, feeling myself being shoved into the right motions by Artie, toward whom I felt curiously grateful. I mean, another day, I would have been in heaven because he asked me at all. And I would have worried about talking to him during the dancing, because he never said anything of his own accord. But now it was an advantage that he was so silently intent on doing the steps properly. If I had a heart attack, he'd push me through four allemande rights before he noticed anything.

"Everybody swing your own." Daphne hadn't said anything. Not even in the Grand Right and Left, when we passed closely enough to give her the perfect chance. Maybe there was nothing to say. And maybe she was saving it. God, what was happening to my senses?

Then old Cottheim announced a fox-trot, the last dance. There was a big scramble while the boys ran around looking for the best deal available and the girls sat on the chopping block, trying to imply a promise of some secret, hidden pleasure, some unknown delight. Unknown and nonexistent. But dance with me, and give it a try.

Jay Huber got mine. He stood directly in front of me and said, "May I have this dance, Jane? It's a social. The last one." I knew that already. I just got up and started to get into Mrs. Fox's dancing position, but Jay wasn't doing that yet. He was busy wiping his palms off on his blue jeans. It took a long time. I decided to do the same thing on my blue jeans even though I didn't need to.

When we finally got to dancing, Jay said to me, "Did you ever see a moth bawl?" It was his standard opener when he asked you to dance. The flying lox box would come next.

Ina danced by with Ape-Man Peters. She waved to me from behind his shoulder blade. We passed Nancy dancing with Joe, stooping over him so she wouldn't seem so tall. Nancy waved too.

I wished I were any one of them. Even one of the drips who had to dance with the teachers because nobody ever asked them. I wished I were anybody else except who I was, a walking sicknik with a terrible secret.

I kept thinking of the variety of mishaps which could happen to me tomorrow morning when I had to sneak off to take my insulin. How could I be certain that I would awaken before the others in order to have the bathroom to myself. What if someone was pretending to be asleep and watching me the whole time? Daphne. Or Judy. Or anybody. What would happen to me if they found out? What would my mother and father do?

"What flies, smells like lox, and is in the shape of a box?" asked Jay, stepping on two of my right toes.

"A flying lox box," I said to him in disgust.

"Rats," said Jay. "Foiled again." Tough. I didn't feel like fooling around with him. If only he would just dance.

"Goldstein," he said to me, "you used to be all right in math class but now you're a pain in the neck." Why didn't he shut up? I wished the dance would get over with. But as my luck went, they always made the last dance longer than the others. A little dividend.

"Gold-stein," he crooned, bending over so that his mouth was close to my ear, "would you break a leg so I can shoot you?"

It was a mistake to have come here.

❋

I awakened and listened, my senses taut. Had I overslept? There was whispering. Could I have missed my chance to be alone to inject myself? Were they up already? I strained to see, but the unfamiliar room was deeply black and the chapel of wooden beams which formed the ceiling stretched upward in endless midnight. Someone giggled. No. It was too soon. I had slept only a short time. A nap. They hadn't even gone to sleep yet. I turned over. The iron cot groaned. Someone giggled again. I pulled the sheet over my head and tried to go back to sleep. I was afraid that bats would fly into my hair. All the others were sleeping with scarves.

Suddenly I was awake again, my heart pounding in my chest, sitting straight up in bed, startled, trembling. There was no mistake this time. The steely gray of dawn was beginning. Many times I had rehearsed this moment with my mother. But now it was really happening. And soon it would be over. Either way, the end was almost here.

I turned on the flashlight. The weak, yellow beam blinked un-steadily. Now open the suitcase, the special combination lock. The numbers, branded on my consciousness, slipped obediently into place. Two-one-five. For my birthday. Click, click, click. The latch sprang open. An imitation alligator case, a gutted manicure set was next. Main Event. The injection equipment. It slides right into the pocket of this special new bathrobe. A perfect fit. It wasn't easy finding a girl's bathrobe with that size pocket.

I shivered in the dampness as I lighted a path with the flashlight to get me to the bathroom door. The cabin, unheated during the winter, had not yet been well warmed by the sun. The intense chill of the early morning seemed a bad omen. My slipper struck an overnight case. There was a thud and a scraping.

"Quickly. Run away," a girl called out. I stood still, terrified. "Now run," she said again. I strained to see who would advise me to flee, one hand protectively covering the broad opening of my bathrobe pocket. But my classmates lay docile and asleep, recklessly limp on their cots, everyday airs gone, forsaken. Someone was dreaming.

In the dark cubicle with the rusty door barred, hidden from those who deeply slept, I took my insulin. And when I had finished, I broke my syringe by smashing it quietly against the porcelain sink. Then I collected all the pieces of glass and threw them, along with my new bathrobe and alligator insulin case, into the bottom of an old rusty trash can which stood in the bathroom.

I returned to my bed and fell back to sleep. Things were going to be different from now on.

CHAPTER EIGHT

There were a lot of things that I wanted, but dying wasn't one of them. I meant to change the way that my life was going, with every day wrong and the following day worse than that. I meant it with my whole heart. But I never intended to die. Or to come quivering so close to it.

I was trying to get my mother and father to stop asking God what they had done to deserve the affliction of their child, me. Wasn't it obvious that I was the one who had the affliction? But they acted like they thought they had it.

It was in the Bible, they told me, that if a man sinned against God, He would give their children's children a bad deal as punishment. If they believed that, why couldn't they figure out that maybe old Great Grandfather Goldstein of Blessed Memory did something and that they'd better shut up about it before the maid finds out and tells?

For myself, I didn't feel like blaming God because I ended up with a dilapidated sugar system that was permanently on the blink. And if I wanted to inquire about why I had such prominently poor luck, that was my own affair.

I was tired of listening to them pretend that diabetes was a wonderful disease. And that if you were going to get something, diabetes was the best one. Allergies, they said, were itchy. Who would want *them?* And if my hand had been deformed, then I'd never be able to play arpeggios on the harp, darling. A child with rheumatic heart disease, remember, has to sit sulking on the side-lines while all the others play games and run after the ball.

If only I would appreciate my particular luck. After all, I could have had a simultaneous case of scarlet fever and African sleeping sickness. With a side order of mumps. But what I got was diabetes. A good, clean disease. One which let's you forget it's around, allows the people you're with to be comfortable. That's nothing to turn your nose up at. So don't knock it.

Clearly, I needed an action which was drastic. Nothing less would work. Because together they were a fortress of steel, and next to them my reasoning was weak, my mightiest threats without weight, my despair earning only their disdain. I was, they implied, a bad sport. I wasn't playing the game properly. And I was insolent, to boot.

When I returned from Valley Farm, for instance, with my syringe, needle and insulin conspicuously missing, nothing much was said about it. I was prepared for a fight to the finish in which I would tell them that I was fed up with this treatment and that either they changed their minds about how terrific diabetes was, or they had seen the end of their cooperative, secret-keeping daughter.

But I never had the chance. That's what was so confusing about having this disease. They never did what I expected.

When it was time for me to take my injection the following morning, the entire set, insulin, hypodermic, needles, down to the alligator carrying case and the bathrobe with the big pocket were replaced. Pffft. Magic. And hardly a word was said about it. A fighting word, that is.

"Your allowance has been cut in half until you make up the price of the various items which you . . . er . . . left behind on your overnight, Jane."

"I didn't leave anything behind, Daddy. I threw it all out."

"Be that as it may, you will receive only fifty cents a week until it all has been paid for." It had nothing to do with diabetes, you understand, it had only to do with replacing what was missing.

My cry was but the tapping of tin on a gong made of steel. It was the chirping of a sparrow, drowning in the thunderous roar of a summer storm. More than anything, I needed to summon their attention; to cause them not merely to look at me, but also, to see.

But I didn't set out to die.

※

When I got to the party, I immediately noticed every candy dish in the room. There was a dish of peppermints. Pale, pastel discs arranged in a circle on a glass plate with a silver rim. A pink one, a white one, green, yellow, orange. They were lying on each other

in overlapping circles. Who would break the symmetry by removing one? Who would? I turned my head quickly away.

Then I saw the bowl of chocolates piled six deep, which sat on
the coffee table in the living room. I studied the deep brown
shapes, drawn with a hypnotic intensity. There was a cherry on
top, And a nougat, just underneath. The little square might be a
caramel, but it also could be a loser like one of those jellies, for
instance. I hadn't tasted a single piece of chocolate since I'd become
diabetic. But I hadn't forgotten.

"This isn't for me, by any chance?" asked Daphne, fairly grab-
bing a square package from my hands.

"Oh yes, Daphne. Happy birthday." She was wearing a beautiful new dress, all striped, with some metal stuff running up and
down it. The back was cut out low and you could see a lot of skin
and freckles and protruding shoulder blades. She was lucky to have
Mrs. Wladecki for a mother.

I had Mrs. Goldstein and I was wearing my old black velvet
warhorse with the cap sleeves and baby's bib of moth-eaten, dis-
colored lace draped onto the neckline. The lace was my grandmother's. Let us all say Amen, Lord. And Hall-e-lu-jah.

"Listen, Jane," Daphne said, propelling me down the hallway
towards the party noises. "Artie's for me. *I* invited him and it's *my*
birthday."

She had guts, that Daphne. A pure case of guts. But I simply
shrugged at her as if I couldn't be less interested and said, "It's still
a free country, I hear."

The party room had a dish of toffee squares covered with
powdered nuts, another of red and black licorice, and a third bowl
which held giant squares of chocolate, broken into individual
pieces. There were other things like potato chips and popcorn, but
I never really cared about anything besides the candy.

"Sit down, Jane, we're going to play spin the bottle." We never
played anything else.

"Hey, Daph," Jay Huber called. "Is your father home?"

"They're both around here somewhere," Daphne said reluc-
tantly. She didn't like to admit it.

"T-o-o bad," Jay returned, looking stricken. As if all his plans
were hereby ruined. What a liar. He had no plans. I knew him
well. I moved over in the circle so that no bottle except for one

doubled in half like a pretzel could put Jay and me out in the hall together.

My new seat was directly in front of the table with the chocolate squares. It was as if the candy had a power of its own, offering itself to me. I am going to eat this candy, something within me spoke. I am going to eat this candy and all the other candy too. No matter how hard I try not to, I will end up eating all this candy. I reached out.

It wasn't on my diet. No. And I hadn't taken enough insulin today as part of my secret game. Even now, before I put a hand on anything forbidden, I wasn't feeling very well. Where, oh where, was the sense of it? There'd only be a big scene with all my friends frightened and huddling together. And then everyone would know. Every person here. And they'd tell every person in their family. The whole world. I took the biggest piece I could see and put it in my mouth.

"It's Jane and Artie," someone shouted. Judy clapped her hands for us. Nancy giggled and hugged herself. "Fixed," Daphne said. Artie and I walked out to the kissing hall not exactly looking at each other. I don't know why Daphne was such a poor loser; she had been out with two boys already, once with Artie. The chocolate was warm and thick and hard to swallow.

The hallway was pitch black. "You ready, Jane?"

"I guess so."

"What's the matter with you? You're supposed to like me."

"I like you, Artie. Only . . . I have . . . I have something I want to tell you about. Something serious. It's a disease. A serious medical problem."

"Well then, we don't have to kiss, Janie. I mean, we could pretend we did." I am invisible and the world is deaf. Listen to me, Artie. Mother, Father. Listen to me. Is there anyone who will ever listen to me?

"Kiss," a voice commanded, and a flashlight beam covered our heads. It was Michael Prindle, looking seasick because he wasn't wearing his glasses, who was stationed there to make sure everybody did what they were supposed to. We kissed.

"Now kiss me," demanded Michael, sticking out his myopic mouth. "Mmm. Chocolate," he said.

For the eating part of the party, Daphne's mother had a big birth-day cake with lots of yellow icing flowers on it, cold soda, and two large bowls of ice cream surrounded by little dishes of wild things to put on top. I evaluated each selection as I waited in line. There were cherries and nuts; three sauces, chocolate, butterscotch and a bright, white marshmallow; colored sprinkles and some tiny red candy hearts. I would have them all.

I was thirsty. The candies were beginning to taste alike. I avoided the ones I remembered not liking; chocolate covered raisins, for instance. And malted milk balls.

"Don't eat so much candy, Jane. You'll ruin your appetite for dinner," joked Ina, helping herself to a delicate serving of butter-scotch. I could drink the ice cream. There would be some that was melted at the bottom of the bowl. It would be cold. And wet. It would put out the fire in my throat.

"Artie," said Daphne, suffering from a sudden attack of radi-ance, "I have something very personal to tell you. Something personal about me." She spooned some nuts onto her ice cream.

"Care for a flower on your cake, Jane?" offered Mrs. Wladecki, cutting.

"Please."

"Anything the matter, dear? I hope you're having a good time."

"Yes, Mrs. Wladecki. Fine, thank you. I guess I was just thirsty."

"Thirsty? Is that all? Well, here's a Coke, dear. You should have said something." I drank the glass of soda in two gulps. A shocking avalanche of pointed bubbles stabbed fiercely at my mouth, pierc-ing the thick, dry taste of diabetes. Relief. But only for an instant. I wanted another. And another. I could have finished all the Cokes intended for this party. And all the other drinks in their closet. And the beer in their refrigerator. And the milk.

But instead, I spooned out the liquid ice cream at the bottom of the serving bowl and made my way to the circle where my friends were eating.

"That's enough," I thought to myself. "I will soon be very sick."

"I have a secret," said Daphne, still on the same kick, "that only Artie is going to hear." Pleased, she laughed to herself.

"Shape up, Daphne, will you?" said Peter. "Secrets aren't polite. Anyway, you don't have any. If you did, you'd have blabbed it all over by now." I felt like lying down and closing my eyes. I wanted to say something but it could wait a little longer.

"Yeah, Daphne. Put up or shut up. We don't like all this fooling around." That was Jay. He looked over at me for congratulations. "Right, Jane?"

I nodded. Speaking would have been easier if I could have been lying down. My breath was not coming out properly and there was something pressing hard in my head just above my eyebrows. Soon I would have to lie down.

"I have a secret too," I said, "but I'm going to tell it right out in the open." There were groans and someone said, "Another one. What is this, a new party game?" It was hard to breathe. My heart was racing.

"I have diabetes."

"Yeah. And my grandmother has leprosy."

"What's diabetes?"

"It's what I have. A sugar disease."

"*That's* the secret?"

"Yes. And soon I'm going to be very sick. Right here."

"Is she kidding?"

"Maybe she's not."

"Funny, I don't think she is." Unrest. Was it possible? Was someone starting to hear me, to listen at last? Could they see that it was true?

"I'm afraid. She doesn't look right."

I'm sorry, Mother. I had to tell them.

"Get Mrs. Wladecki. Run."

And Daddy. I'm sorry for you, too.

"Jane. What is it? Here, lie here."

I had to tell.

"Where's Mrs. Wladecki? Hurry. Look at her. She's sick, all right."

You wouldn't listen.

"Will you still love me?" I asked the descending curtain of darkness. "Now? Will you still love me now?"

✻

I swam through fields of blazing red wheat, through an eternity of narrow tunnels lined with searing spikes, bobbing from one tip to another; wounded, impaled.

Somewhere through the moist green sea, there were voices on a dune.

"When she wakes up, I'm going to tell her right out. You've got diabetes. Otherwise she'll think she's dead, like I did."

"She already knows, smart aleck. She already knows. I've seen her here before."

I opened my eyes. There was a round-faced boy, dotted with freckles, leaning out of a bed to have a good look at me. In a bed just beyond, I saw Moose, the boy who hadn't been able to take his own injection. There were other beds with boys and girls in them, people I had never seen before. Maybe I was in a dream. At an overnight. At Valley Farm. Maybe. And maybe I was back in the hospital. I closed my eyes and swam away.

A frowning doctor with wire glasses sat down next to my bed. He carried a large pad of paper and used a pen which wrote with India ink.

"I'm going to ask you a few questions, Jane. You can hear me if you try. Wake up, Jane." I waited for him to go away. "What day is today?" he persisted. I tried to figure it out. He didn't like waiting. "Can you tell me what day it is today? Or not?"

"I think Sunday," I said, finally.

"Very well," he said, not revealing whether that was right or wrong.

"But the newspaper will tell you," I added.

"Er . . . yes. Now repeat after me: Eighteen ninety-nine, Whitestone Bridge, the Noble Duke of York."

"Eighteen ninety-nine, Whitestone Bridge, the Noble Duke of York."

"What are you doing here, Jane?" he asked. "Why are you here?" I closed my eyes so that I wouldn't have to see him and then I said, "I wanted them to notice me. But I didn't want to die."

❊

They didn't scold me, or act annoyed, or make any mention of my allowance. They hugged me and kissed me and called me their baby. They brought me books to read and baskets of flowers and fruits which I couldn't eat, but which we distributed to the children who had things wrong with them other than diabetes.

They came only during the regular parents' visiting hours, and didn't try to sneak in at other times. They didn't insist that the nurses do too many special favors for me like bringing extra blankets because my feet were cold, or opening the window because my feet were warm.

It was a miracle. They didn't seem to mind that I was on the

Pediatric Ward this time, or that all the nurses and doctors and the other children knew that I had diabetes. Mother played gin rummy with me any time I asked her to, and once she even played a hand with a little girl across the aisle who had a kidney disease with a tube and a bottle and a very strong smell.

"I've had a number of talks with the doctor," she said to me on the day that they removed my intravenous feeding. "And it may be that we weren't looking at things from quite the right angle." She touched the swollen place where the needle had been. "I don't know why we can't begin again, do you? A little bit better this time, perhaps?"

It was a wild hope. The most. But she had to be serious about some of it, because even now, certain important things had changed for the better. I wished long life and good health to whomever had been talking to her. He had done well.

That night at visitors' hour, they brought Susan with them. Susan, who was only nine. Whose tender age barred her from ever setting foot on the Pediatric Ward.

"We sneaked her up the back stairway," Daddy whispered proudly, and together, we introduced her around to my various roommates. The next night, they brought Aunt Bertha, who told the whole room about her gall bladder operation. And the night after that, they came with Mrs. Wladecki and the joyful message that Daphne was permanently through with Artie and forever devoted to a Third Former at another school whom she had seen in the elevator of her apartment house.

"Moose," I said the following afternoon as we both received supplementary insulin shots, "did you ever hear of a summer camp they have for diabetic kids?"

"Yeah," he admitted cautiously, "I heard of it."

"If we both got to go there, you and me, then we'd each have a friend. I mean, I'd have you, and you'd have me . . ."

"Yeah?"

"Don't you think it would be an advantage? Knowing each other? Not being completely strange? Without worries about figuring out how much insulin to take, whether you're doing things right. Just eating whatever they serve. Like here in the hospital. What do you think, Moose? Sounds good, doesn't it?"

He turned his back to me and pulled the covers over his shoulders. "Sounds swell, Jane. Swell."

Come on, Moose. Give it a fight. You can't just give up like that.

You can't. I said, "Then you'll ask your mother? Will you, Moose?"

He didn't move. And then he said, "Jane? Do you ever shut up?"

Beyond, the gentle winds carried the scent of springtime boldly into the antiseptic air of the hospital ward; the two mingling tentatively, existing together.

But then the magic of the breathless new season surged forward. And there was nothing that I wanted more than to drink it in.

THE VERY IMAGE OF A CHILD
By Kathleen Lukens

CHAPTER ONE

Martha woke early thinking of Dr. Menapage of the Health Department and the interview to take place on that day.

She was afraid of interviews, afraid she did not make a good impression; but Phil wouldn't take off from work to go so she would have to go alone. Nothing would ever move her husband to excuse himself from work, not even the time she fell and broke her arm in two places, not for Billy's graduation from high school, not even, Martha sulked, for Patsy's chance to go to school. He was getting old, he had said, and fearful for his job. But he never took off from work even when he was young.

Martha didn't mind getting up. She always sprang to life after six hours sleep like a fan being plugged into the wall. This morning she was already nervous about calling the taxi, getting Patsy bathed and dressed, and making it to Dr. Menapage's office in the County Office Building by eleven. It was only eight now. Breath struggled out of her tight lungs unnaturally. Whenever she thought of breathing, she always seemed to lose the habit. She sighed. Her heart raced just a little.

The rain that had wakened her during the night, rousing her to shut all the windows, had ceased. A faint, tepid light seeped through the glass making the curtains look dusty. How Martha hated dirt! Cleanliness provided her with a sense of purpose in life, making her sail joyfully through the grimiest of chores, yet making her wary of tender shadows, animal odors and people who failed to notice them. She was about to get up and brush off the curtains when she saw Patsy lying by her side.

Instinctively, Martha stroked the sparse, silky blond hair of her little girl's head and tried to think of something nice to say. Affection always made her stumble self-consciously. How strange she always felt when Patsy would crawl into bed beside her and melt right up to her body without her noticing. What a pleasant strangeness. Billy had been limp and pliable like that when he was newly born. The doctor said it would always be Patsy's way.

"Mommy's going to fix it so Patsy can go to school," Martha sang. Six-year-old Patsy who had her head curled down toward her belly in rest, fluttered the almost nonexistent lashes of her birdlike eyes.

"Up, baby," Martha chirruped, erupting from her bed of sheets and blankets in one bold leap like a porpoise rising from the sea, "Bath time!"

They called them "unfinished children." Martha tried viewing Patsy with the detachment she felt Dr. Menapage might assume while the hot water tumbled into the bathtub around the curled figure of her daughter. Laughing now at some bizarre mental picture of that phrase, Martha acknowledged to herself that Patsy's depressed facial bones and her underdeveloped nose did rather look like a cake that had fallen in the middle. She rumpled Patsy's hair and Patsy smiled.

Then Martha felt anxious again and depressed. Her stomach rumbled and gurgled, recoiling with little points of pain. No, Martha corrected herself, fearing as always the halo effect of love and expressing as usual her need to denigrate that which she felt to be her own. Patsy looks like a frog. The child winced though her mother said nothing. Patsy waited for the tightened lips to smile.

A frog, Martha suffered, her eyes staring through the warm mist in the bathroom at the roll of pink toilet paper framed by the immaculate tiles of gray. They all do, all mongoloids, high-grade or not. Through the corner of her eye, she caught the too-large, yellowish skin crinkling on her daughter's back, the stumpy arms sprouting from her sagging shoulders, the bulbous belly floating out in front, the spindles of her legs.

Martha turned and observed for a split second Patsy's rounded face, the bulge of her forehead, the ripple of her nose, the too-big tongue or too-small mouth, the deep indentations at the corners of her eyes, the fishlike speckled jellies of the eyes themselves. And now, alas, the expression of offended trust and desired forgiveness that leaped out of them into the cold waste of Martha's heart to set it oozing and churning with remorse.

"C'mon, baby, let's scrub," Martha offered with a strained smile that pressed her daughter like a kiss, smoothing out the wrinkles on her forehead and the ones barely hidden behind her eyes. Patsy's face settled down into mild interest and pure rapt adoration, the familiar expression she wore, when near Martha, with mindless constancy.

"Mama," she spoke in her low froggy voice, the froggier the more endearing now to Martha, who responded to need and guilt as others respond to love.

"We're going to see Dr. Menapage. We'll see if he doesn't like you in your pretty new dress."

Martha lay Patsy out on the bed to dress her the way an undertaker lays out a corpse. The child had learned to stay perfectly still while her mother performed all the small tasks of buttoning, covering, zippering, and buckling. Martha had been warned by an Association pamphlet not to do as she did but rather to encourage independence, but Martha was forty-six and as she put it, "too old to learn patience at this stage of the game." Besides, it wasn't just Patsy. She admitted to herself that she took a certain pleasure in doing for others what they hated to do for themselves: ironing a fresh white starched shirt for Phil every day and, before he left for school, another one for Billy; cleaning their soiled shoes every night; finding their lost articles and books like a faithful bird dog retrieving game.

The taxi came a minute late but Martha had allowed an extra fifteen minutes to meet such an eventuality and ease her compulsive esteem for time. They climbed into the back seat, Patsy smarting from the sharp edges of her stiffly starched frock, the tight buckles of her patent leather shoes, the heavy scrubbing given her tiny ears. Martha set her face into a serene mask and tried not to care that the driver approached intersections with too great speed, that her own coat was perhaps a bit shabby, that Patsy might not remember to keep her tongue inside her mouth. Ten eternal minutes later, the county courthouse.

They arrived twenty minutes early. Martha decided in favor of sitting in the small park near the gray stone building with its high Doric columns rather than appear anxious to Dr. Menapage. They study you as much as they study the child, someone had told her. She hated sitting. Her palms sweated. From overweight, she decided. Not from the tremble in her stomach, her anticipation of the interview, the unbounded torture that was to come. Would he agree to Patsy's going to school? Patsy had been eligible for a

year now. "Just read the laws of the State of New York," the
man from the Association talked to Martha as if he were sure she
never would. "And tell that principal what is what."

Actually Martha never had to do any reading at all. Her neighbor, Mary Trumbull, told her there was a special class for re-
tardates at the Oakwood School in Westfield, and that Patsy had a
right to go. Mary wasn't too clean, in Martha's opinion, but she
was a college graduate and nice, considering. The local public
school where Billy had gone professed ignorance of the special
class until Martha tried enrolling Patsy with them. The idea of
putting Patsy in class with normal children brightened them up
considerably, Martha thought, just as Mary said it would. Only
now they said Patsy was too young.

The Association literature had declared that schooling was necessary even for children like Patsy. Otherwise Martha would have
just accepted the public school judgment. Didn't they know best?
Besides, getting pushed around, as Mary called it, just didn't seem
to bother Martha. What bothered her more was the idea of being
thought of as a troublemaker or Patsy being thought of as a blight.
She'd sooner clean bilges, scrub all the pots in the Waldorf, go
hungry for a month, than try to converse with Dr. Menapage.

They waited another thirty minutes inside, Martha combing the
pamphlets on Social Security benefits to better advise her own
aging mother, Patsy staring down at the floor striking her heels
backwards against the walnut bench in the anteroom. When she
finally was ushered into the doctor's marble and steely gray office,
she found his face pleasantly virile, florid and intense. A muscular
hand held the pen writing on his desk. He wore a rich-looking gray
flannel suit that sprouted an immaculate collar. Not a single hair
poked out of place.

"Excuse me," he said without looking up. He finished the form
he was filling out.

"Oh," he forced a smile when he finally faced them, "she's a
mongoloid."

Martha nodded.

Menapage grunted.

"Uh, pardon me," Martha said timorously, wondering whether
she should offer her hand, "I'm Martha Bullitt. This is Patsy, my
daughter."

Menapage grunted again. Down's Syndrome, he was thinking.
What's the public school system supposed to do with kids like
that?

"I was told to bring Patsy to you for an examination. We need
your approval . . ."

"What's the point?" Menapage asked gruffly.

Martha blushed.

"I mean in sending somebody like her to school? Not that she
isn't a wonderful child," he remembered at last to be kind, "but is it
reasonable to expect the schools to act as baby-sitters, Mrs. . . .
eh . . ."

"Bullitt."

"Mrs. Bullitt? It's well established medically that these children
can't learn until they're at least ten, if then. It may even be harm-
ful . . ." He could've said they're not even human and cited
Sergio Levy's post mortem cerebral dissections to prove it, but he
dared not hurt this woman with the truth. Her hurt, he supposed,
was probably great enough.

Martha told herself she had grit when it came to solving family
problems. Why not now? "The Association for Mentally Retarded
Children doesn't agree with you," she answered in a voice almost
inaudible with fear.

A bunch of laymen, Dr. Menapage sneered privately. Should he
bother the gray-haired, rather large-boned woman in front of him
with explanations, he wondered. Would she understand about the
extra chromosome in Trisomy 21? Would she care? "Mrs. Bullitt,"
he tried, "mongoloids tend to deteriorate right after birth and do
not come out of it until about five. Mentally then, they're about
two years old. Should a two-year-old child go to school?"

"No," Martha was agreeable, "but Patsy's six, nearly seven."

"Mentally, she's two."

"Dr. Finger said she had a fifty IQ before she had her strabismus
corrected. He thinks she'd do better now."

"I doubt that," Menapage snapped. "The best I've seen is sixty
and that one was much bigger than this one . . ."

"But size doesn't . . . the smaller children are often brighter
than . . ."

"Besides," Menapage said with what he hoped was finality,
"they don't live long, ten years or so, so why bother?"

The first time Martha had heard that argument it struck her like a punch in the stomach. This time it thumped against the dried scab of her resistance. "The Association says that's misleading . . ."

"Misinformed do-gooders," Menapage mumbled under his breath.

". . . based on the high infant mortality rate," Martha ignored him though her heart was thudding in her eyes. "So many die in the first year of life. But once they've passed the first year or two, they live to be twenty-five, thirty-five, forty-five, thirty years on the average."

Patsy melted into her mother's lap and tried not to hear the unpleasant exchange that centered on her.

"Weave [leave]," she whispered, "my mommy, my lone [alone]."

"I have an obligation to the people of this country and state, Mrs. Bullitt," Menapage said suddenly without ever really looking at Patsy, "I'm sorry but I can't approve Patsy's application at this time."

Martha fled Dr. Menapage's office on the edge of tears, Patsy clinging to her arm, trying anxiously to see her mother's eyes. A tall, big-boned woman, Martha moved so swiftly toward the park outside to conceal her shame that Patsy literally flew off the floor as she struggled to hold on. Outside, the mother thumped down on the park bench and attempted to regain composure. Patsy melting into her lap against her breasts. Through the dews of sorrow, Martha beheld butterflies, dogwood blossoms, the noonday light, Patsy's curious face confronting hers, red and unlovely, the hair ribbon sliding off her wispy band of hair.

"Well, baby," she sniffled, "I can't think of any reason why we can't have an ice cream soda, can you?"

✳

The hill was a hill of fire when the sun crept under it. And in the dark came the lightning bugs to catch in the cages of her hands. Patsy screamed with delight, bending her knees and jumping skyward; she'd call out to Martha " 'ightnig bugs" until all things melted and darkened for the moon.

They had seen the geese making their landing on the pond behind the courthouse and turn and face and sail in the same direction.

"Duck," Patsy had commanded, "duck. C'mere!" Lifting her hand into the oily bread wrapper she had sown the lake with ecstasy and bread. Then the geese had come sailing toward her gliding like the ships of her who called, pecking at each other to snatch the crumbs, Patsy rolling joyous on the shore.

Then, away! Her small feet trailed them into the brack water ooze, her hand reaching for a water bug but finding a snail. "Bye, duck," she cried, and reeling on her small, weak, wobbly legs, she fell into a sea of dandelions, rolling, singing, laughing, picking until her hands shone with the summer's burning blossoms.

❊

Nine-year-old Jimmy Trumbull came over at 8:30 the next morning to inform Martha that his mother, Mary, had a virus and would she be a pal and mail a letter for her on Martha's daily trip to the store. Martha agreed, scarcely suppressing her delight at her neighbor's indisposition. For it not only gave her an opportunity to call on Mary for her informed opinion of Menapage's views but a chance to repay her neighbor by washing and ironing her laundry. Not that the above ideas sprang openly and consciously into Martha's mind. By precept, Martha believed that hard manual labor and cleanliness outranked intellectual wisdom by a geometric ratio. She would take, for example, the medical opinion of a nurse with a clean house over a doctor with a dirty one any day. An untidy professor could never compete in wisdom with a carpenter fresh from his bath. Indeed, by precept, friendship itself was a waste of the working day. If she offered to do Mary's laundry, she told herself, it was to show Mary how laundry ought be done.

Martha greeted Mary Trumbull's green-gray pallor with her usual glow of affectionate concern. She pressed a pamphlet on intestinal viruses from the Gotham Life Insurance Company into Mary's drooping hand, and subtly laid another on food poisoning prevention on Mary's coffee table. Then, "Let me do your wash," she offered with the same tone of unbridled generosity someone else might use with, "Here's two tickets to a Broadway show!"

"Gee, thanks, Martha," Mary answered with a yawn, "you're a peach."

Martha paused a moment waiting for Mary to ask about Menapage but the younger woman only sneaked a furtive and longing glance towards the bathroom by the parlor. Martha gathered the laundry up to leave.

"Say," Mary Trumbull stopped her on the threshold of the house, "what ever happened with Dr. Menapage?"

"Nothing," Martha answered, stepping across the doorway. She felt suddenly guilty now that Mary did as she had wished. Mary didn't look well enough to be wise.

"What do you mean 'nothing'?" Mary called weakly after her. "Did he uphold the superintendent's decision or not?"

Martha halted with the enormous load of laundry in her arms. "No," she turned and called, "I mean yes."

"Hell's bells. C'mon back," Mary cried in more salubrious timbre. "Let's hear the bad news word for word." Controversy was to Mary Trumbull like a drink of the waters of Lourdes.

Martha, protesting, was obedient. She sat down in the disordered living room as far from an ashtray full of dead cigarettes as she could manage inconspicuously and proceeded to tell the content of the interview as simply and objectively as she could. If anything, she embroidered Dr. Menapage's comments to make them seem more logical and considerately put than they actually were. She hoped Mary would agree that further resistance would be futile.

"OK," cried Mary shaking off her grip as easily as a dog shakes off a dousing. "It's either the family court or an appeal to the commissioner of education. Let's figure out the best strategy . . ."

It's the lawyer talking, Martha mused with sinking heart. For the moment she had almost forgotten that Mary Trumbull spent three years in law school before she met and married Hank, bore four children, and set herself up as the neighborhood legal aide. By precept, Martha disapproved of lady lawyers, not being able to imagine any woman wanting to play Perry Mason when her children needed haircuts and the house hadn't been painted for the past five years. Yet here she was seeking Mary's advice again, accepting the notion that unless Mary ran out of suggestions she had not done all a mother ought to do for her child, and finding her neighbor, despite her eccentric attitude towards homemaking, rather pleasant company at that.

"The trouble with going to the family court first," Mary was thinking aloud, "is that the judge's decision is final. Now, if we appealed to the commissioner first and he turned us down, we could still go to the family court."

"God, I could never go to the family court," Martha wailed. The idea of being Perry Mason was frightening enough, but to be one of his badgered witnesses! "I wouldn't know what to say. Everybody'd stare at Patsy . . ."

"So what?" answered Mary, who always seemed to forget that Patsy was a mongoloid. "She's cute as a button. Anyway she wouldn't have to . . ."

"I couldn't," Martha's soft brown eyes watered with anticipated humiliation, then with shame at having spoken her fears aloud. If only Phil would assume some of the responsibility for Patsy's problems, she thought, her mood shifting to anger and resentment. He's the one who believes in people's rights.

"OK, the commissioner it is. I'll write for an application right away." Mary deliberately and mercifully ignored Martha's show of distress. "Martha," her face glowed like an ad for *Life and Health*, "we're going to win this thing because we're right."

Martha could not suppress her pique at Mary's attitude of righteousness. "Well, I'm not so sure," she rejoined testily. "Why should everybody else have to pay for my mistakes? She *is* retarded. She doesn't look like other children. I don't blame people for not wanting to hire a baby-sitter to solve my personal problem. It only makes them resent her, don't you see? I made my bed, aren't I the one who has to lie in it?"

Martha picked up the laundry before Mary could answer and prepared to flee.

"Sit down!" Mary Trumbull looked directly into Martha's confused expression. "She's not a mistake, she's a child. Because the people of Warren County, New York State, and God Himself, believe one child is worth as much as any other, and they all have the right to an education. Because your child's affliction was by chance. It could've happened to anybody, and any civilized society sees its responsibility to . . ."

Martha turned away as Mary climbed into the rarefied ether of abstraction.

"She's better off home with me, with someone who loves her," Martha got up and bolted through the door, leaving the laundry behind.

"Do what you want," Mary Trumbull threw up her hands and looked greenish-gray. "But give a little thought," she jibed as Martha quickly retrieved the laundry and set out across the lawn, "to the dependent child who outlives her devoted mother."

※

Phillip Bullitt believed in a strict division of labor between the sexes. Not that he thought about it. It just never occurred to him to help Martha with the dishes, change Patsy's or Billy's diapers when they were infants, or do the family shopping. An electronics engineer who had not obtained his night-school degree until he was thirty-eight years old, he was an unremitting student in his chosen field, a dilettante in literature, history, and economics, and a man who preferred his own company to anybody else's except when he was in the mood for Martha's.

Although he had married Martha nearly twenty-six years before, he had never ceased to congratulate himself on his excellent choice of mate. Martha had endured the ups and downs of his abortive career as a small businessman, all the while keeping a spotless house, making few emotional demands, and never bothering him with the children's problems. On the whole, Phillip tended to think of his wife as a woman of great and mysterious inner strength, the archetype of all the motherly feminine qualities, the incarnation of generosity, charity, decency, unalloyed by pettiness or pride. Indeed, if Martha ever threatened to belie any of the haloed characteristics he assigned to her or promised to rebel against his changeless views of her nobility and strength, Phillip conveniently tuned himself out that his illusions might remain intact and undisturbed.

It caused Phillip no end of bewilderment and irritation, therefore, when Martha began to impinge on his picture of what she was. After all, he told himself, her stoic bearing when the child's defects were discovered and when its limits were made known, had only served to dispel any need for his involvement. Now, suddenly, Martha had become querulous and accusing, claiming for herself a certain timidity in dealing with the school authorities, insisting he help her make decisions about Patsy's future, demanding he take an interest in the child.

Loving peace as he did, Phillip set out the very next day after supper—it was spring when the sun is generous with light—to take an interest in his daughter, and found her to his surprise an amiable child. To anything he suggested, for example, she was immediately agreeable, *yes* doubtlessly being her favorite word. She could not cut with scissors, he noted mentally, but she could hum a familiar little tune—and nicely at that. She could tell her father what a cat said. And she could do an imitation of her dog.

Having thus warmed to his unexpectedly weightless chore, Phillip looked to Martha for her approval as he saw her emerge from the kitchen and move towards them, this father and daughter conversing at last in the garden.

"What a big wose!" Patsy was throwing up her hands, dancing and making silly gestures over her father's batch of Scarlet Beauties, meanwhile snatching with devilish glee a fistful of flowers.

"Yep," Phillip seemed almost not to mind the havoc Patsy was wreaking in his garden. "That rose *is* getting big," he agreed. "It's getting so big, in fact, I'm going to send it to school come next September."

" 'Chool?" Patsy screamed as if she understood his joke. She roamed the garden, clapping her hands crying " 'Chool."

Phil leaned his elbow on the carpetlike lawn, lit a cigarette and turned toward Martha, who, with her back to him, was vigorously shaking rose food on the Goldens. "Quite a kid," he volunteered expansively. He then waited for Martha to be kind.

Martha turned towards him, not approvingly as he expected, but with the frenzy of a lioness shielding her cub. "You needn't make fun of her, you know," she shook with rage. "What a dumb thing for a father to tell his child!"

Phillip went pale. The apparent discrepancy between his performance and his good intentions momentarily stunned him. He began, "I was only trying . . ." but then he stopped.

Rising, he brushed past the child returning to his newly proffered warmth, strode up the steps into the big, gray house, the screen door slamming in his wake.

"I told you," he muttered, "I don't know what to do with children."

✳

Patsy ran with her dog before the sun, slept with its fur for a footrest, made him beg, aped his bark—he laughed like her—so warm the inflections of their love.

The world spread out over her and from it she withheld nothing of herself. There was no distinction between the earth and sky. No bounds to the sea or to the shore. The sunset happened. Water ran. The roses sweated in the morning. Birds flocked to the feeder if you remembered the seed. When words failed her, there was more than the silence.

She named her dog Ruth after her favorite doll, and fed him soda pop though he wouldn't drink it. Patsy could color, though not within the lines, sing "Mary Had a Little Lamb," first stanza.

On the monkey bars she could "skin the cat." In her mirror she could catch the summer morning. She could count all the stars of the evening on one hand and announce to her mother, "That makes five."

Patsy feared only loneliness, anger, disappointment, the sleep of the giants who held her in their trust. It was good to pound pegs with a hammer, know red from blue, watch her mother cut paper dolls from a big, fat book called Sears and Woebuck.

She tasted mud to see how it tasted, and wished for a piece of ball gum. Morey Trumbull had a cat but he would not let her feel it. She must remember to push her tongue back in her mouth.

To her, the perfect shape of everything had been prepared. In everything's truth she believed. Of death, lies, time she knew nothing, this ill-made child, as if her world had been lighted by eternity.

✳

Mother always makes too much of me when I come home from school, Billy reviewed Martha's fuss over breakfast with the critical judgment of youth. He poked without enthusiasm at the eggs and bacon fried to crisp perfection. Dad must wonder, the psychology major told himself, as he turned to his father with fresh perspective.

Phillip, unaware that he was being analyzed, was engrossed in the newest copy of *Electronics Monthly*. He let his coffee grow cold in front of him. Far from envying Martha's attentions to her son, he had not yet noticed that Billy was in the room.

✳

"Phil, drink your coffee," Martha shouted at him as she refilled the sugar bowl.

Phillip groped for the coffee and obeyed.

Writhing on his seat in discomfort, Billy stewed. She really oughtn't talk that way to Dad.

"Phil," Martha shouted again impersonally, like an alarm clock ringing. "Speak to your son who just came home from college."

Billy blushed with embarrassment, then with anger. He tossed his silver into his plate dramatically and prepared to protest his mother's nagging his father, when Phil suddenly turned to him and asked, "What time is it, Bill?"

"One o'clock," Billy answered weakly.

"The opera!" Phillip jumped to his feet and lunged for the

Zenith. *"Rigoletto,"* he beamed in Billy's direction as he fiddled with the dial.

"Dad, I . . ." Billy started to speak.

"With Gigli," Phillip interrupted. "Shhh, wait a minute till I find it."

"Can't you talk to your son for five minutes?" Martha plunked down at the kitchen table.

"Gigli was the greatest tenor alive . . . terrific recording," Phillip shouted at Billy from his spot by the radio. "Better in my opinion than Caruso . . . I *am* talking to him, Martha."

As Billy finished his breakfast coffee, his mother looking on adoringly, his father glued to his post beside the Zenith, he offered, "Mom, you know you might like opera if you ever really listened to it."

Martha rose. Stacking the dishes with feigned wrath, she said, "If you think I'd waste my time listening to a bunch of screeching roly-polies with T.B. all afternoon, you're as crazy as he is."

"Mom," Billy called after her as she turned her back to wash the breakfast dishes. "People your age," he exuded pontifical wisdom, "should share each other's interests."

Martha smiled compliantly and returned to her work. Patsy had come into the room and was curling up contentedly on Billy's proffered lap. He was stroking her hair and calling her "Funny Face" and "Patsy Small." He's a good boy, Martha mused, but he'll find out when he gets married.

The dishes all washed, wiped and put away, Martha sat down to converse with Billy. The strains of a soprano aria leaped from the Zenith in assaultive decibels.

"Did I write you about the interview with Dr. Menapage?" Martha hollered across the table. "For God's sake, Phil, turn that down!"

"Yes and frankly, Mother," Billy answered with sophomoric omniscience and at the top of his lungs, "I don't think you really want her to go." Billy's accusation, made more strident by the sudden drop in the Zenith's volume, charged with brutal force on Martha's senses.

"Don't want her to go?" Martha choked. Tears came to her eyes. "After all I've been through." She fled down the hall into her room.

"But Mom," Billy called after her. "Mom, I'm sorry." He

dumped Patsy off his lap and marched past his father toward the
garden. Phillip's head was swaying gaily to the theme of "La
Donna è mobile."

"Goddam opera," Billy muttered.

❋

Martha did not stay long in her room. She was too painfully aware
of the agony of guilt to inflict it on others. She found Billy in the
garden and before he had a chance to apologize she explained that
she had been taking diet pills all week and this made her weepier
than usual.

"Honesty," she repeated the timeworn cliché, "is good for the
soul." Yes, Billy was right, she did not want to force the issue; she
did not want to make them take Patsy into school. Having made
her confession to herself, Martha sighed and waited for the relief of
catharsis to come, but it dallied and did not appear.

Billy had curled up for an afternoon nap in the hammock swinging between the apple trees. Martha sat. The familiar strains of the
sextet from "Rigoletto" wafted into the rose garden and Martha
thought how it wasn't bad at that. Actually she had known for a
long time that she did not want to fight with the Board of Education's decision. It was not that she had been dishonest with herself.
It was more that she was afraid. Afraid, and ashamed of her fear.

Billy is a good boy, Martha mused. He forgets that Patsy is a
mongoloid. He thinks of her as a little girl throwing cookies to the
birds or trying to find the cricket in the garden. And Mary forgets
too. She sees her as a famous case, Martha thought, as the what's-
his-name . . . Dreyfus of Buckminster Lane. And Phillip? I wonder if he sees her at all.

Suddenly aware of her own body, Martha looked down to discover Patsy nestled against her breast, having fallen asleep in a
matter of seconds. She felt the animal warmth of the small child's
body, the prickles of tenderness in their points of contact, the wish
very close beneath the surface of her skin to hide, encompass,
shield this fragile child within the mountain valleys of her love.

The sweat of Patsy's sleeping trickled to the tip of Martha's
breast like the milk of nurture. But it grew cold. For Martha had
passed beyond the comforting contact of her own senses into her
objective mind, into the world as she fancied others saw it.

Now she saw the scorn in Dr. Menapage's eyes; the revulsion in
the principal's pained attempt to smile; the patronizing grimace of

the superintendent. And now Patsy was revealed through their perspective, as Martha thought they saw her child: the small round ball of her head with eggs of eyes, their lids eternally inflamed; the dazed expression; the furrowed tongue that crept from the cave of her mouth; the short, broad neck; the flat, square hands; the protruding belly; the "monkey" feet. She heard the shy, low stammer of Patsy's speech; the silly aping and snickering Patsy evinced at the merest smile, the slightest yield of their harsh, almost fearful, mask of judgment.

"Dull," "defective," "infantile." Martha remembered the cold indifference of their verdicts. Yes, she recalled, they had been detached. More aloof than hateful, scornful, cruel. Contempt would have been more human. A tornado, typhoon, an act of God, it was as if Patsy were a somewhat more trifling natural disaster. Ah yes, now she remembered. Patsy had not been human to them; she was, therefore, not worthy of a human reaction. The doctor had called her "an interesting process," Martha reflected bitterly, "a something-or-other chromosomal aberration." She remembered him referring to "the" toes rather than "her" toes, to the loops on "the" fingers, "the" teeth that had failed to erupt in Martha's child.

Martha shivered. She was afraid. Afraid less perhaps of what they might inflict upon her child than what they might do to her mother love. For Martha was conventional. She did what was appropriate to do, felt what was appropriate to feel. She feared the world's contamination of her caring, society's mute decree that she not love what was not lovable, that she be not drawn to that which, by its judgment, must repel. Could she cling to her own warm feelings against the referendum to reject?

She looked down now at the pale lids closed in sleep, and her warmth returned. Out of her need to be needed, in the lumpy, graying egress of middle age, this child had come to her to lie upon the breast so long unsought. An ugly child, a joyful child, a stupid child, a loving child. And now, at last, alas, if the world would let her, an eternal child.

❋

Billy drove Patsy and his mother to Rockhaven, agreeing twice to go inside only to be told "never mind" when they finally got there. "You shouldn't send a boy on a man's errand," Martha said peevishly, the barb intended for her absent husband who had not taken off from work.

Billy had turned east off the Interstate Parkway where Rockhaven rose before them like a reef in an ocean of undulating hills. Martha clucked appreciatively at the neat, brick, Georgian cluster of buildings that reduced life to a single, clear, consistent pattern. She marveled at the trim cemetery rigor of the lawns, the tombstone monotony of the identically shaped buildings. This might be an institution for mentally defective children, Martha told herself, but some solid thinking was behind it.

Dr. Douglas McLeod, neurologist and noted researcher, headed a team of diagnosticians at the state institution. Some three thousand mentally defective youngsters had passed under his scrutiny over the years, some of them children of local residents, most children who dwelt in Rockhaven. It was Mary Trumbull who had insisted that McLeod would know best whether Patsy ought to go to school or not.

As they drove into the tidy parking lot, Billy noticed his mother's rising spirits and prepared a wisecrack on the rapture of modern sanitation. But he changed his mind. After all, he thought, suppressing the desire to twit the gentle woman who sat beside him, Martha had made and broken the appointment with McLeod twice already; although thanks to her ubiquitous concern for other people's feelings, she had developed a virus with a high-grade fever on the first occasion, and sprained her ankle on the second. At least she could be certain, Billy mused, that the doctor hadn't suffered as much as she had.

Good old Mary, Billy thought affectionately. It was Mary who had insisted on a psychological report before she applied for an appeal to the commissioner. She had reasoned that the eminent neurologist had seen enough profound defectives in his time to raise Martha's hopes about Patsy rather than to dash them. McLeod's staff could provide the Bullitts with a complete work-up on their child, including the psychological tests, the electroencephalogram, the neurological reports, even a psychiatric evaluation if one was needed. Besides, Mary confided to Billy, even Martha wasn't deaf to so much wisdom.

Billy watched his mother stroll, Patsy clinging to her arm, down the flower-margined path to the Guidance Building. He studied the straight line of her back, the marching shoulders, the balanced gait. They moved with purpose and, strange for Martha, with a flow of grace. She might have been, he thought, a native woman bearing on her head a massive burden pridefully. She's doing it, he beamed, she's doing it. Calmly, rationally, against her primal wisdom and her holy silences, she moved from view, her son turning with a twinge of love for home.

*

Billy looked at his watch. He had allowed them over two hours already and there was no sign of the bulky gray-haired woman and her mongoloid child. He'd had lunch, read two chapters of *Delinquent Youth* and heard an inning and a half of the ball game. Too bad the Ford didn't have a radio. He imagined himself going through the psychological tests with Patsy. She'd know all the animals and what they say, he thought proudly. After all, brother Billy taught them to her himself. Too bad she doesn't know the colors, he thought. Everything's got to be "wed" or "boo." Or the body parts. "God, what a nitwit!" He chuckled aloud as he thought of his mother trying to get Patsy to wash her eyes and Patsy pushing the cloth around her ear. Cripes, he hated waiting. Too bad his summer job at St. Joseph's Shelter didn't start until next week. He was really going to understand those delinquents. Too bad Dad didn't come with Mother.

Billy heard the laughter of children over the hillock to the west, started to open the car door to investigate, when up the path with skinned knees and her hat askew came Patsy, Martha puffing in her wake. The young man leaped from the Ford in a second flat, twirled Patsy around him once and swung her unceremoniously into the car. "How'd it go?" he called to Martha before she had even climbed the hill.

"Fine," Martha answered, flushed and smiling. "For Heaven's sake, open the car door for your mother, Billy," she huffed good-naturedly. "I'm talked to death."

Martha plunked herself down on the front seat gracelessly. The car lurched forward, toppling Patsy off the back of the front seat across her mother's body exactly as the child intended. She screamed with glee. Billy looked irked at the distraction to his driving.

"Oh, let her go, Bill," Martha responded to his frown. "Today, she's been a very smart girl."

Martha sighed as if with relief as they rolled out of Rockhaven, spotted a Scarlet Tanager flying across the parkway, discoursed on the glory of the season.

"What'd he say, Mom?" Billy broke in abruptly.

"Oh, Dr. McLeod," Martha answered distractedly. She seemed rather pleased with herself. "He said Patsy has a very good vocabulary. I mean, considering."

"Uh-huh. Swell."

"He said she has a very good self-image. That means . . ."

"I know what that means, Mom."

"And she's well taken care of, and obedient. He called her 'a marvelous child' and he meant it."

"And?"

"And, well, and that I'm a very good mother." Martha cleared her throat and tried to sound nonchalant.

"We know all that, Mother. What did he say about Patsy going to school?"

"Oh, nothing. Maybe he'll mention that at the evaluation in two weeks."

"But what about the appeal?" Billy sounded more than a little peeved. "You did talk about the appeal to the commissioner, didn't you?"

"Well now, Bill," Martha answered distantly, "there's no real rush about that, is there?"

"No rush," Billy nearly screeched. "I thought that's why you went to McLeod in the first place."

"Patsy is doing so well at home with her own mother and with people who love her, and she's so young," Martha petted the corn-silk strands falling over Patsy's tiny ears, "I think we'll just wait a little bit."

"Holy Nose," Billy muttered all the way down the parkway up over Powell Drive to Buckminster Lane. "Holy ear, holy ass."

❋

It was Martha's sudden gush of high spirits in the week following her visit to Dr. McLeod that cut through the fog of Phillip's inattention.

That Saturday in July Phillip looked up over *The Harvard Business Review* and listened to Martha singing in the kitchen.

"What d'ya say, Bill?" he addressed his son, who was reading in the hammock. "Think your mother's fallen in love?"

"I think she's nuts."

Billy's waspish answer stung his father.

"Listen, Buster," the elder rejoined indignantly, "let's hear you

talk about the woman I love with more respect. Just because she's
been your goddam maid and vassal . . ."

"Sorry, Dad. Sorry." Billy pulled up a lawn chair like a salesman
who had been looking for an approach, "But you don't seem to get
what's going on."

"I get it, Your Lordship," Phillip sucked a cigarette and snorted
pure and righteous fire.

"No, you don't, Dad, and I'm going to tell you . . . Mother is
neurotically attempting to gain a sense of self-esteem by not sending Patsy . . ."

"Don't give me that Freudian baloney about your mother. Your
mother is the kindest, most generous, open-hearted . . ."

"I agree with you, I agree with you. But if you'd only take a
good look at what this . . ." He was going to say, "what this saint
is doing to her child," but thought better of it. ". . . What this
good woman is doing to herself."

Phillip picked up *The Harvard Business Review* and tried to become reabsorbed. That kid hasn't been able to find a decent thing in
human nature since he took up psychology, he thought.

"Dad, listen," Billy pulled the periodical from his hands.
"Please," his voice broke just as Phillip planned to damn well
snatch it back.

"Dad," Billy repeated slowly. "You've got to make Mother see
that Patsy has to go to school. You can't let her hide her from the
world."

✳

Martha studiously avoided Mary Trumbull the week after her visit
to Rockhaven. When Mary finally caught her hanging wash in the
back yard a few days later, Martha brushed off her inquiries about
McLeod with: "He's a wonderful man, Mary, and I'm so thankful
you sent me to him. I'll tell you all about it real soon. As soon as
I've finished sewing curtains."

Indeed, Martha sighed with relief when she heard that Mary was
masterminding a small band of neighbors who were opposing another group of neighbors opposing a Negro family's moving into
Buckminster. Not that Martha felt strongly one way or the other
about civil rights, it was just that now Mary would be too preoccupied with this issue to insist on making Patsy's appeal. It did
distress her somewhat that Billy spent so much time following after
Mary "like the sorcerer's apprentice," Martha thought. He kept

huckstering her causes, dragging Patsy with him all over the neighborhood gathering signatures on Mary's petition, calling that nice Edith Roberts a "bigot" and a "racist." But then she reassured herself that this must be something psychology majors did, like understanding juvenile delinquents.

Meanwhile, Billy had felt a bit disloyal discussing his mother with Mary Trumbull but Mary had brought it up first, and besides she was the only person in Buckminster Lane who ever even heard of a defense mechanism. Indeed, he felt doubly damned when Mary told him he was too hard on his mother. Martha's sin of omission, as Mary saw it, was in not recognizing and using her right to send Patsy to school. "If you don't use your rights, you don't have them."

Patsy detected through the constant and excited use of her name that she was somehow the center of a great event. She tried thinking of what she wanted for Christmas in case that's what it was. How she loved having Billy carry her on his shoulders all over the neighborhood, especially to the Trumbulls, where she finally got to feel Morey's cat. One day, a bald-headed man tried to tear up Billy's piece of paper and Billy grabbed it back and they ran together giggling straight for home.

Phillip prepared to take off from work the day of the evaluation. He just called the night before while Martha was doing the dinner dishes. "Hello, Steve? I'm taking off tomorrow. Family business. Thanks."

Strolling over to Martha who thought her ears had short-circuited, "Hon," he said with mock nonchalance, "you do want me to go with you, am I right?"

"Phil," she cried throwing her arms around his neck, "of course I do," though a second later she was not so sure. Carrying Patsy upstairs for her evening bath, she wondered why her husband had suddenly decided to become concerned. How much did he know about Patsy anyway? Had he ever read any of the literature from the Association she kept sticking in between the leaves of *Electronics Monthly*? It would have made her feel strange and inappropriate to start telling Patsy's father about Patsy all at once. She dared not affront his newfound interest.

Phillip had great tolerance for the individually private mode, but, unlike his son, he told himself, he had no wish nor need to penetrate these inner mysteries. People wanted what they said they wanted, acted as they chose to act. If people failed their good intentions, he reassured himself, it was only because the real and the ideal are hard to reconcile. He quoted Browning to himself, lovingly, "Ay, but a man's reach should exceed his grasp or what's a heaven for?"

Data Processing lay on his lap untouched. Upstairs he heard Martha running water in the tub for Patsy's bath. It was not that he did not recognize the conflict raging in the human heart, he mused. He saw the conflict for what it was: good struggling with evil, love versus hate, anger opposite kindness. The Good Man would in the end surmount the evil. The Evil Man had let the bad take charge.

To suggest as Billy did that love might be in conflict with itself was sheer nonsense. How like a Freudian, he thought angrily, to deprive good of its storied purity, to deny the holiness of the heart's affections. The idea that Martha might love her child and yet choose to stop her growth was monstrous. Ridiculous! How could one give, take, build, destroy at once?

He glanced expectantly for a moment at *Machinery* magazine sitting on the end table beside him. How could love do anything but heal? He thought for a moment of his own rejected childhood. People love or they do not, he tried to content himself. Those like himself who do not know how to move tenderly towards others stay out of the way of those who do, or resort at last as he did to amiable abstractions, to "brotherly-lovisms," he gently mocked himself, to principles like Justice, goals like Truth. Ah, but those who love, he thought warmly and the image of his Martha came to mind, they need no abstractions, no principles, no Truth. Theirs is the gift unalloyed.

He would go with Martha in the morning not because of Billy's arguments, he mused, but because she needed him and it was time, he supposed, to get involved. He smiled knowingly at Martha's being flattered by the doctor's compliments. How she underrated herself! How odd that she should expect all others to be blind to her value except him. And yet everyone saw. Take Mary Trumbull, she saw Martha's virtue. He liked Mary, not his idea of a woman, mind you, more a colleague. She was practical. Her ideas moved him more than Billy's. What would become of the child if Martha died?

Dr. McLeod was a busy man but he gave the Bullitts an hour,

the time he thought they needed. Martha traced Patsy's early history: the child's characteristically more promising appearance at birth than at six months, her quiescent, undemanding infancy yet the look as if her world had shattered when Martha left the room; the discovery of her thyroid deficiency; her inability to eat regular foods until she was five; the slowness of her development including her first tooth at eighteen months, her first attempt to stand at thirty months, her first word at twenty-nine months, her first sentence at four and a half. She raced into the present, daring to extoll Patsy's curiosity about everything alive, her fondness for dancing, her joy in mimicry and pranks, her lack of ill-temper and ill-will, her desire to try new things, the sliding pond for instance, though her body often failed her. She focused in her consciousness the image of her beaming child, listed the nursery rhymes she'd learned, spoke proudly of her ability to listen to a story being read, praised her manners at the table.

The white-haired doctor finally began, "Patsy is a very agreeable, stable, obedient child, for which you can be grateful, for not all mongoloids are. What is most striking about her, however, is her high intelligence, high that is, for a child with Down's Syndrome."

Phillip glowed and pulled his chair closer. Martha seemed somehow less impressed.

"Our psychologist, Dr. Mason, puts her IQ around fifty-five or sixty, a relatively mild retardation that places her in the company of some four or five percent of children of this type; educable, I'm happy to say, Mr. and Mrs. Bullitt."

"But Dr. Menapage?" Martha's face was flushed. "He said she's mentally two years old."

"Well, Dr. Menapage has been out of medical school for a long time, I suspect, Mrs. Bullitt. In the old days, statistics on mongoloid IQ's were almost always derived from institutions. Medical students tended to be taught that all mongoloids were profoundly mentally defective. Now, however, we know that these children with the most common chromosomal aberration have mental ages up to seventy. In fact, mongoloid-looking types with another form of chromosomal anomaly even have normal intelligence. I'm afraid my colleague in the health department suffers from the common prejudice."

"IQ's aren't really stable anyway, are they?" Phillip put in.

"Very good, Mr. Bullitt," McLeod replied approvingly. "Patsy's excellent vocabulary is undoubtedly more a reflection of the environment you've created than her innate potential. On the other hand, she probably could have learned to perform better with the blocks and the form board if you or your wife had provided her with more challenges in that direction. Patsy's typically hypotonic, ill-coordinated, but she should be able to tie her shoes and button her coat."

Martha prickled with a blush of shame.

"The school won't let her in," Phillip said bluntly. "My wife, here, has taken Patsy to the principal, the superintendent of schools, and finally to Dr. Menapage and they all seemed to agree that Patsy can't be taught."

"There's something about mongoloids not being ready to learn until they're ten and then they don't live more than ten years and . . ." Martha began to elaborate.

"Oh yes, I know that argument, and it's absurd. I know Dr. Miraglia in the commissioner's office and I assure you he's more sophisticated than that. Get a lawyer and arrange for an appeal. I'm sure they'll take my word for Patsy's ability."

"Thank you, Doctor," Phillip was preparing to leave.

"I don't . . . I don't," Martha stammered, "I don't want Patsy going where she isn't wanted . . . I don't want her hurt . . . I . . ."

"Mrs. Bullitt," the thin doctor leaned forward over his gray steel desk. "Institutions are impersonal. They don't want or not want. Patsy's teacher in the board of special classes school will be delighted to get her. Any child as amiable as Patsy . . ."

"Why," Martha looked up and demanded, "should the taxpayers hire someone to solve my problems?"

"Excuse me, Mrs. Bullitt, didn't you say you had a son who graduated from high school two years ago? Did he go out for extracurricular affairs?"

"Yes, but . . . ?"

"Which ones?"

"Track, for one," Phillip put in. "He was the Eastlake medalist in pole-vaulting."

"Dramatics, school newspaper," Martha added. "What's that got to do . . . ?"

"I just wanted to show you he was a special child. That is, the school system was willing to spend rather large sums of money on special services for him and a relatively few other children who wanted them." Dr. McLeod moved closer to his point. "Take the football team, for instance. It uses up a lot of money for very few students, but most schools would not think of not having one, and the taxpayers would not dream of not supporting it. Why should they object to giving a less fortunate child like Patsy the key to life itself?"

Phillip straightened up and took on an aura of greater dignity than he had had when he entered the room. Martha's mood failed to change.

"I think," McLeod said with conviction, "that you should send Patsy to school whether the authorities want her or not. You've accepted your child unconditionally, Mrs. Bullitt, you've done well, but, there's another world that only gives to those who earn . . ."

"Patsy's different," Martha nearly burst into tears. "She can't be like the others."

"Not entirely different, Mrs. Bullitt," McLeod replied. "You see, all children need to be loved without condition up to a certain age. But they also need to know how to respond to the demands of growing up. They need to learn how to think, work, create, how to make demands on themselves."

"But Patsy . . ."

"Patsy may never, it's true, fit into that world completely. She may never achieve the capacity for an independent life. Even some bright people never do, in a real sense, that is. But it's ridiculous for the school authorities to argue that Patsy can't grow and develop because her intelligence is limited. Even if this child is never good at arithmetic, she can learn self-reliance from other children and her teacher, Mrs. Bullitt. And how to create love and respect in those who will not love her simply because she is."

Martha tossed and turned that night until the dawn stars ceased to burn and the mists grew thick upon the grass. Patsy's happy. My love is good, she told herself. I haven't asked anything for myself.

Phillip's profile glowed pink with the color of morning. He snored and his breath made his nose-hairs quiver to his thunder. She was tempted to wake him and ask: isn't love always beyond one's control? Must it not always be a blessing? Phillip heaved over on his side, rolling like an oak log, and she did not wake him. Everyone, she mused, sees love as he feels it and only as he feels it.

She wondered sadly if her husband's love wasn't something assigned to whoever provided him with care, in gratitude. Had he ever cared to know what she was like? There are different ways of loving, Martha mused. That's what McLeod had tried to say.

Martha flopped over on her stomach, found a small hole in the pillowcase with her hand. Picking at the hole until she tore it, Martha wondered: Had she not let Patsy believe that nothing within herself, no tasks she performed, no challenges that she met, had value in themselves? Had she not really led her to believe that even the power to create love lay beyond her strength, for it was there whether she created it or not?

Patsy needed more training, greater strength than normal children. She needed power to brave contempt in the eyes of strangers. There had to be something that made them look beyond her open mouth and reddened eyes and find in her a little child.

School? Martha wondered now whether Patsy ought not go. Hadn't McLeod implied that there are things a child can learn better from those who don't love him than from those who do? Where approval is reward rather than a gift?

The sun erupted in the east waking the morning glory on the wall. And Phillip curled in sleep around his woman.

※

The summer faded. Through the window, Martha watched the roses' wilted glory. She sighed. This morning, she would go, her Patsy, her face lit with expectation, her thoughts no further than the marshmallow cookie she'd seen Martha packing in her lunch.

The irony, Martha groaned. She could not bring herself to smile. The irony of loving a child nobody valued, to make by that very loving the value of her. There's no safety, Martha mused, no guarantee, no assurance of need and thus of love. Even the salve of self-pity she must deny herself, for while Patsy was not normal nor ever would be, she was not wretched either, surely not monstrous or grotesque.

Then Martha smiled at last. Patsy was stuffing Ruth into her lunch box, the dog trying desperately to escape with the cream-cheese sandwich in the bag.

"Mommy," Patsy cried, Ruth leaping up out of her arms,

rushing the screen door and bursting through the space into freedom, "Wuth won't come to 'chool."

"No, Baby," Martha answered, tightening Patsy's loose barette, "school's for boys and girls. Ruth says he'd rather wait with me."

"I'll tell him he can come," Patsy sprinted into the rose garden leaving Martha to find curly black hairs in the cream-cheese sandwich, to toss it out and begin repacking the lunch.

The appeal to the commissioner had succeeded, Martha reflected, thanks to Dr. McLeod's intervention, Mary Trumbull's prompt and decisive action, and the second-guessed submissiveness of the superintendent of schools and the school principal. Only Dr. Menapage persisted in the assertion of his right judgment and he had been overruled. Yet, even though the school was expecting her, the bus rolled on its way and Patsy had been prepared, Martha could not be certain that she could permit her child to venture forth that morning from the sanctuary of her love.

Mary Trumbull was already on the porch summoned, no doubt, by Billy. Morey and Jennifer Trumbull were joining Patsy in the chase after Ruth and Martha fumed and fretted that Patsy would fall and soil her new pinafore before the bus came into sight. She could hear the dog yelping and imagined Patsy already rolling in the grass, the two Trumbull children undoubtedly dressed like ragamuffins egging on the child in dotted Swiss.

Martha slapped the jelly over the cream cheese, rustled the sandwich into waxed paper, added another cookie, and closed the lunch box. She daydreamed of Patsy weeping through the window of the bus, "Please, Momma. Please don't send me."

Then suddenly a horn blew once, and Martha, dashing for the porch, found Billy buckling Patsy, grass stains on her pinafore, behind the seat belt of the station wagon bus. A farewell committee of the Trumbulls, Billy and Phillip were waving good-bye to a little girl delirious with joy. Martha had to burst through the crowd to give her her lunch.

In three seconds flat, the bus had gone, Patsy never looking back, the dog never whining once, the adults never breaking their train of talk. Martha hurried into the house, threw herself on the sofa weeping, "The bus came early. The bus came early," not knowing whether it was the child's departure, the grass stains, the hairy lunch or Patsy's nonexistent tears that had done the most to break her fragile calm.

"Ah, there you are," Phillip slammed the screen door behind him. "I almost thought we were going to miss the bus."

Martha did not get up.

Phillip went over and sat down by the crumpled body on the sofa. He patted the back that was turned towards him. "Don't cry, darling," he coaxed sympathetically. "They're going to teach her a lot of things we can't, a lot of things she's got to learn."

"Who cares?" Martha's head lurched up and looked accusingly at Phillip. "Who gives a damn?"

Phillip stared directly at the smeared, wet, reddish profile of Patsy's mother with a twinge of anger. "Martha," he said testily, "I used to think you wanted to protect her. But now I believe you are more afraid the world will value her too much, too much at least for you."

Martha looked straight ahead at the white flowers on the couch cover. Her husband did not know it but she suffered the chill of his accusation like the warming rays of the September sun. So he knows my weakness, she told herself. He sees my imperfections. And he cares at last. "I wanted her to grow," she agreed with her new-found protector, "I wanted her to grow but not beyond me."

She didn't have to be strong anymore, she mused, waiting for him to break the silence. She was free to wish for the wrong things for her child, the weak things, because her husband, Phillip, would point out the right things and see to it that she did them.

Phillip only lit a cigarette.

"I wanted," Martha tried to provoke him, "I wanted her to stay the way she is."

"Uh," Phillip only smiled. "Then why did you send her?" He finally asked pleasantly, "Honey, we would have supported you no matter what you decided." A woman like Martha can never really be wrong, he was telling himself, "Her first day can still be her last."

Martha righted herself on the couch gracelessly like a large child thumping to an adult position. She began stacking the papers on the table to disguise her profound disappointment.

So I do have to be strong, and right, and reasonable, she thought sadly. I can't just love the child. I always knew I couldn't. I even have to make the wise decision.

"I sent her because she's not a thing," she snapped at Phillip. The game was up. "Because it's what one does with a child."

"Because you love her," Phillip took on his old look of mindless admiration.

"No," Martha answered numbly. "I sent her because I needed her not to go."

"Needed her not to go?" Phillip repeated the words aloud. He must ask Billy to unravel that one. Martha carried the papers into the kitchen.

"Because you taught me without intending to, that it's better if people can love you for what you are than for what they need you to be."

FOR THE BEST
By Carol Panter

CHAPTER ONE

"Listen, Julie honey," said her Uncle Bernie into the receiver while noting the closing Dow Jones, "whatever happens to that baby happens. It's God's will. Your aunt and I are just thankful that you're going to be all right." His secretary signaled that she was holding a call on another line.

"Look, sweetie," he said gently. "I knew you when you were knee high to a grasshopper, right?"

It was true. "Julie baby, watch out. Your king's in danger." His voice was the same as it was then, in the days of flannel pajamas and plaid woolie bathrobes, and creaking leather bedroom slippers with special arch supports. His warning came to her now, across the fading years. "Listen to me, honey. If you move that man, it's all over. I'll jump you from *here*, and I'll jump you from here. Now keep your hand on the man and take your time. Reconsider." His wisdom had been constant. She had always followed his advice.

"That's right, Uncle Bernie," she said. "You were always my best uncle. You know that."

"That's exactly why I'm telling you now, Julie. You get over things like this. You won't think so, being right in the middle of so much worry. But I'm telling you. It's your old Uncle Bernie talking, honey. Did I ever steer you wrong?"

"Never, Uncle Bernie. You never did."

"Then remember this. Maybe that little baby was never really meant to be, Julie. It's not our place to question God's will. Whatever is going to happen will happen for the best." His secretary flashed impatiently.

"By the way, honey, I'm having them send a nice basket of flowers over there. To cheer you up."

He was her best uncle from long ago, but this was today. Numbly, Julie said, "Thanks, Uncle Bernie."

"Uncle Bernie wants the baby to die," she said to Harold when he came. "He said it in every way except right out."

"So what?" he answered. "They're all crazy in your family, Julie. You knew that."

"But you'd think they'd have the decency at a time like this to restrain themselves."

"Forget it, Julie," Harold said, moving the heavy visitor's chair closer. "They don't know what to say. It wouldn't help any if they did. There's only one thing that counts right now, and that's that little boy of ours and whether he can muster the strength to make it."

"Harold?" She had vowed that she wouldn't cry for him. "Do *you* want him to die?"

Harold sighed. Did he want? Did he want? God, what could she know of what he wanted? He wanted her, his wife. Julie, independent, with eyes clear and shining, teasing him, daring him, stopping only long enough to share her flash of joy. Harold, quickly. You must see this. Harold, listen. I want to read you something.

When her time was near and she stood before him, frail, with her skin stretched taut about the blue-veined igloo in which grew his son, he had wanted to help her, to offer her his strength; the weight seemed so heavy. But she recognized his thoughts and would not allow him to dwell.

"Harold, you silly thing, you're jealous, that's what you are. You really wish that you could carry this baby yourself. I don't expect you to admit it, but I know it whether you say so or not. You wish that you were the one that were having our baby."

"I do not, Julie," he protested, laughing. "I do not."

What was it that she was asking him now, only without the playful challenge in her voice, with only the tight struggle to hold back a torrent of sorrow from rushing forth, spilling everywhere? Did he want the baby to die? That baby? Theirs?

"I do not, Julie, he said. "That's our baby. I most certainly do not."

Then she broke the vow and cried and cried.

✳

Julie spent most of the day watching with sad, still eyes the billowing configurations of clouds in the kaleidoscope of the failing autumn sky. She looked at the groupings as if they had a deliberate significance, a visual meaning. Lying on her side with her face towards the window, she watched the forms drifting apart, joining to create yet another illusion, a wordless spectacle, a reminder of the many mysteries. Always, as the waning beams of sunlight succeeded in their feeble interjection, Julie saw in it a winner, a victor, an ending triumphant.

To the God who now revealed Himself in the sky above the oil stench of the East River, she prayed for her baby. She prayed many prayers, different prayers. Only some had words.

Several times before a priest had visited the other women in her room. On the first day he spoke to her, saying, "Hello. Are you Catholic?"

She answered "No," and wondered if he thought she might be dying. The priest continued to greet her even after she had declined his services. Then he would disappear behind the drawn curtains of the women who had accepted.

The idea came to her today as she listened to their muffled prayers and followed the drama in the deepening sky, that maybe there were some *special* prayers that you could say if your baby is very badly defective and hardly has the smallest chance. A rabbi would know. Surely this must have happened before. Somewhere. To somebody.

There was a booklet under her water glass called INFORMATION FOR PATIENTS and Julie read with mounting hope the section entitled *Your Chaplain*.

"Through the cooperation of the religious associations of three major faiths," it said, "a chaplain of your faith is available on request twenty-four hours a day for prayer, counsel, and the administering of sacraments and rites."

She would ask him to pray with her, to recite the prayers which her ancestors had spoken when their hearts had been greatly laden and their hopes independent of reason.

A man answered, a deep, friendly voice, "Chaplain's Office." He would help her. He would join with her, strengthening her cry. They would pray together.

"Excuse me, please," she said. "I'm a patient on the maternity floor. I'd like to see the rabbi."

"I'm sorry. The rabbi is only in the hospital on Fridays."

On Fridays. For a moment she couldn't remember. But then she knew. Today was Monday.

"But do let me take your name and have him call you. He checks in with us every day."

"No," she said, hardly able to speak. "I needed him now."

✳

With gentle hands and the softest of voices, they moved her to another room, a larger one, with beds in it for four. She was the only occupant.

"Good-bye, dear," said her original roommate, who was nursing her fifth. "Good luck. I hope it all turns out all right."

The new room was better because now she could be alone with Harold, but still she heard the wheels of the bassinets coming and going in the hallway and the hungry cries of the babies rooting in desperation for the comfort of their mothers.

When Harold came that afternoon, there was a doctor waiting at the doorway to Julie's room.

"Are you Mr. Walters?" he said to Harold.

"He's here to tell me the baby died," Harold thought. He was suddenly afraid. "Yes?"

Why was it so difficult to ask? A simple question, is the baby still alive? Was there a kind of betrayal in the mere asking? A lack of faith in a tiny being who had so little chance of survival? Was there a magic power, as in the childhood story of Peter Pan? Children: if you believe in fairies, clap your hands. Please, children, please clap your hands.

"Yes. I'm Mr. Walters. My boy . . . is he . . . ?"

"He's alive, Mr. Walters, but his condition is serious. I'm Dr. Bing, the Chief Pediatric Resident. I'd like to talk to you about what it is that's wrong with your baby. And with Mrs. Walters, too, if you think she should hear. Otherwise, I would be glad to explain it to you and you can later . . ."

"No," said Harold, pushing open the door. "My wife needs to hear, too. She may have something she wants to ask you."

She looked white and thin and pitifully alone sitting in the corner bed of the empty room. Someone had tied a blue ribbon from the flowers to the end of her bed. Harold pulled the satin bow as he approached. Julie's cheek quivered, her eyes widened with fear. Her husband and a doctor. Did it mean . . .? The ribbon fell.

"He's still alive, Julie," Harold said. She breathed spasmodically, her movement a single, silent sob. "This is Dr. Bing and he's going to give us the details of what's wrong."

"Mrs. Walters, your baby was born with a very rare skeletal defect in which his bones are so fragile that he will sustain fractures at even the slightest contact with another object, even a normal touch. That's why you had such a difficult delivery. Many of his bones were severely broken in the uterus. Others during the birth. Often a baby like this lives only a short time. But sometimes they can survive longer. It's difficult to predict in this case. The fact that he's lived for two days is a good sign, but it will be longer before we know for sure."

Harold wanted to take her home. Here and now. Just put on her clothes and walk out of here with her. Get away from all the hurt, the bad news, the flood of catastrophe. They had a place to go where they had been happy before all this. Together. Just the two of them. He would take her back there, to their apartment.

Harold said to the doctor, "What's the name of the disease, doctor?"

"Osteogenesis imperfecta congenita. It's a systemic disease in which a deficiency in the deposit of bone salts causes the bones and ligaments to be vulnerable to the slightest trauma."

Harold wrote it down in his head. Osteogenesis imperfecta congenita. How pompous it sounded. How terrible.

Osteogenesis imperfecta congenita, Julie thought. First declension, feminine, nominative, singular. She asked, "Is there a cure?"

"None," said the Chief Resident of Pediatrics, Dr. Bing. He was young, as they were.

"What should we do?"

"In most cases, Mr. Walters," the doctor said; it was hard for him, Harold could see it, "a baby like this, if he survives, is eventually placed in a home which can provide the extensive nursing care which he requires because of his deformities and constant breaking of bones."

"Forget about most cases, Doctor, if you will," Harold asked, "and tell me what you would do if this were your baby. I'd appreciate knowing that more than anything else."

Maybe it was too much to ask of him. Wrong, really. What did he know of this doctor? He looked like someone who could have been in his class in college. What, in turn, did the doctor know of the arrogant, venerable-sounding defect called osteogenesis imper-

fecta congenita? Had he ever seen a case before? Did he know of a
family which had successfully managed to keep a child like this at
home?

. . . if it were *his* child. Wasn't it possible that this doctor was
someone who could build a life for a defective child and that he
and Julie could not? Or might the doctor insist on an institution for
their baby because it sounded like the easiest way and the proper
choice for his own home situation? Harold shouldn't have asked.

"My own babies," said the doctor softly, "I take home with me.
No matter what. But that doesn't mean it's right, Mr. Walters." It
was Harold to whom he spoke, but his eyes never left Julie.

"Doctor Bing," Julie said. "He's two days old and I never saw
him." How vulnerable she sounded, how plaintive her plea. How
ordinary her request. A mother wants to see her baby. But of
course. It's expected. Required, even. Except for this baby, whose
mere presence in the world has caused all the oldest rules to
become obsolete. "Poor Julie," Harold thought, "tomorrow her
milk would come."

The two men exchanged hesitant glances. "Let's all go," said the
doctor suddenly. "Now."

✳

"You saw him?" Harold's mother asked that night. "You went?"

"Yes, Mother Walters," Julie said carefully, "he looks like
Harold." Did she shudder? "Did you go?" Julie continued more
directly. "They allow grandparents, I hear."

"No, dear," Mrs. Walters said quickly. "I first wanted to see
you."

She's lying, Harold, Julie's eyes were telling him. Your mother's
lying and you know it.

"And where is Pops tonight? Had a meeting or something?"

Julie, stop it. What do you want from her? She's getting old.
She's unadjustable. She expected to have a normal grandchild. Let
her get used to it. Julie, think. They didn't have anything to do
with it.

Then Julie's parents came, tiptoeing into the room, smiling and
carrying a bouquet of flowers, but with red-rimmed, bloodshot
eyes.

"Mother." She buried her face in the older woman's fur collar.

But quickly she returned to her usual manner and kissed her
father with both warmth and control, and the grandparents were

soon earnestly speaking of a truth which they could barely name and believe even less.

"*Every* bone in his body was broken at birth?" her father intoned incredulously. "It's impossible. How could he live?"

"Most of them don't, Dad," Julie said patiently, now the teacher herself. Words. They were simply words. Nobody understood any of it. "By the way, we've named him Martin."

"Martin." They all tried it. Nobody knew exactly whether it fit or not. For this baby.

"Osteogenesis imperfecta congenita," repeated Julie's mother with undisguised hostility toward the intruder. "How do you spell that?" She removed a pencil and pad from her pocketbook. She had doctor friends, she said. She was going to ask. Words, words, they hung so hard on the words themselves. And in the nursery lay Martin Walters, alive. With every bone in his body broken in the process.

"Who is this Doctor Bing who told you that you could put him in an institution or take him home, whichever you decide? What's his background? Is he an orthopedist? A professor here at the medical school?"

"No," Harold answered. "He's the Chief Resident in Pediatrics, that's all. He's a fellow about my age. Maybe a few years older."

"A Chief Resident? What's that?"

"It means it's his last year of training. Next year he goes into private practice."

"*Next* year? And you're taking his word for it? A decision like this? I say get another opinion. Two other opinions, to make an odd number. I can recommend a very good man, older, the head of a clinic, I met him at a party. Very handsome. I can't think of his name right off, but I'll look it up and get him to come to see the baby tomorrow."

"And I know someone, too," said Harold's mother, not to be outdone. "It's the nephew of a neighbor. An orthopedist. Also an older man, but he looks young. I don't want you to decide anything about the baby until we get this man in to see him."

Harold closed his eyes for an instant. It was terrible when they all got together. It was always terrible. But here it was worse. They continued, energetically arranging for the two additional consultants; one from the bride's side and one from the groom's.

Which specialist would tell them that they'd gotten it all wrong, that little Martin Walters is not the baby with all the peculiar bumps and indentations at the wrong places in his arms and legs; that he's somebody else's baby, a mistake, a terrible error, they should sue, how dare the hospital scare them that way? Which one would? The old one? The young one? The nephew? The nameless one?

Harold said, "Julie's tired. Maybe you'd better go." And then they suddenly reminded themselves of Julie, who had been there all the while, and departed with solemn promises that tomorrow would bring the old ones and the great ones and the ones who would see the truth, but not be able to change it.

*

But he lived, the little goner, he lived. Martin Walters stayed alive in spite of his desperately inferior skeletal characteristics and the prediction that it would be all for the best if he didn't.

And his mother and his father went to see him every day thereafter. And they gently placed their fingers on the warm, downy skin and on the lumps and bruises to soothe him and to offer him comfort. It wasn't the same as holding a baby in your arms, yet they never refused a new offer when the nurses changed shifts, to touch him again, to feel him alive. Did he know, with the mysterious instinct of the newest life, that they belonged to him? Would he ever know?

On the eighth day, they pronounced Julie well enough to leave the hospital world into which she had come to participate in the miracle of womanhood.

The credentials of the physicians who had seen Martin Walters were long and distinguished, they were eminent men of science and humanity; they were fellows and diplomates, academicians and clinicians alike; they were heads of department and professors emeritus. It was, they all said, for the best. No parents should take such a burden into their own home. Their life would be ruined. Part, they advised. Separate. Do not embark on a life together.

Let Martin Walters go.

*

Every night when Harold arrived home at five minutes to six, Julie had something ready for him. Sometimes it was a steak and a baked potato, or spaghetti, or lamb chops or hamburger. Carefully, they would divide what she had made between them. But when Harold's plate was finished, Julie's was always still full.

He would say to her, "I guess if you're not going to eat that, it would be foolish to throw it away." She would nod, and they would exchange plates.

They lived in a brown apartment on Eighty-sixth Street, near Columbus. There wasn't too much furniture in it, and whatever there was, turned up in different shades of brown. The apartment had a promising number of window views, all courtyards, except for the window in the bathroom which looked out onto a yawning gap in the fast column of overgrown dwellings. But there the glass in the narrow frame was deliberately opaque and textured with spidery flowers. There was no way to look either in or out.

Julie cleaned the bathroom every morning. There wasn't much to be done with the window, except for wiping the frame.

She also cleaned the living room and the kitchen, and straightened their few closets and drawers. It all took under an hour.

"Eat something, Julie," said Harold's mother at the Friday night meal. "Force yourself. I'll bet you don't eat breakfast, either. You've got to start every day by cooking yourself a big breakfast." In pantomime, she broke two eggs. "Put the food in your mouth even if you're not hungry. Look at you. You're all skin and bones."

"How like you, Mother Walters," Julie thought, "to try to safeguard Harold's interest." She cut into a piece of pallid chicken.

Julie tried following Mother Walter's suggestion because cooking took up time, and passing the time from one stretch to sleep to the next occupied most of Julie's energy.

Steadily, she eased two eggs into a pan of sizzling butter, adjusting the flame so that they cooked slowly, delicately, softly and thoroughly; just right. When they were perfectly done, she delivered them gently from the pan and carried them to the place which she had set for herself. She covered them lightly with salt and pepper and then, ready at last, she cut into the eggs, engaging a sizeable chunk on her fork.

But then, a great revulsion seized her and she stared, transfixed, at the running, broken, adulterated mixture on her plate; yellow, weeping, bespeckled with peppery imperfections. She quickly took her plate to the trash can and in one certain movement, threw it all out.

Relieved, she fixed herself her usual breakfast of a glass of cranberry juice with vodka and an Arnold's Luncheon Roll. The vodka was good for getting back to sleep. She looked at the clock in the kitchen. It had all taken only four minutes. She wondered if she would go mad.

Sometimes a telephone call from her mother would awaken her.

"Julie? I just saw an ad for a dress in Bonwit's that would be perfect for you. Go down and get it, honey. Charge it to us."

Her mother understood that Julie's problem was one of deprivation, but she could not acknowledge that the deprivation was not one of clothes, nor, as Mother Walters feared, of regular, well-balanced meals.

There was a baby, a little boy, her's and Harold's; alas, the mark of where he had lived and grown was still on her body. She was alone and he was alone. And neither of them were dead.

Perhaps they had been right, the older ones, the ones who were proficient in the taste of eventuality. Wouldn't death have been better? Wouldn't it have been a charitable gift to a baby who lived trapped in the poverty of a blundered conception and a lifespan which was never intended to endure the length of an hour?

Finality, inevitability, *Yea, though I walk in the Valley of the Shadow*, she knew about them; she grew up knowing. If Martin Walters were dead, she would be free to go forward, mourn properly, adjust. But instead, he survived. She could remember how hard she had prayed for it.

It was a grave dilemma, Julie reflected. She was twenty-two years old and was herself destined to live, even if her life were short, for many years to come. And in each year, there were three hundred and sixty-five days just like this one. She could not see how.

A package arrived from a large department store. Beneath the immaculate box and the crisp, shiny gift wrapping lay a three-volume set of books. They looked familiar. The books were black and leather bound with lettering of gold. A place marker of red ribbon was attached at the binding. Somebody was sending her prayer books.

She looked at the card and then, with a detached curiosity, at the first volume of the set. They weren't precisely prayer books, no, but more like a collection of observations; reflections on a variety of topics, but not strictly inspirational. Julie leafed through the gilt-edged pages: *The Value of Education* by Grover Cleveland; *How to Be a Winner* by Vernon Law, Pitcher for the Pittsburgh Pirates.

"No," she thought, closing the book, "wrong girl." She fitted the volume back into the box and carefully replaced the wrapping, slipping the wide white ribbon into place without destroying the bow.

Then she telephoned the department store and asked that the pickup service come to remove the gift.

"Certainly, madam," said the operator. "May we credit your account?"

"I don't have an account," Julie said.

"Then perhaps we can send you something else instead. There must be something else that you could use."

Julie was silent. There was something else; it would be about an even exchange, too. "Do you carry foods, drinks, liquor, things like that?"

"No, I'm sorry, madam. Nothing like that."

It was too bad. Those leather-bound books were expensive. They could easily be traded in for a four-fifths bottle, minimum. She ended up ordering some new handkerchiefs for Harold and three pair of socks.

*

Throughout the bleak winter, Julie returned to her window, waiting. She knew the way the shadows fell in the courtyard at different times of the day; she could feel the ripping, piercing cold of the wind even though it was warm where she stood. She knew the winter sky, filled with bitter strokes of icy marble. She knew that whenever she would again see the caustic face of winter, at another time, in another year, she would taste the anguish of the days in which she waited at her window without end; at twenty minutes to two, at five minutes past four.

She was waiting, she told herself, for Harold to come home. But the restlessness was still within her after he arrived, and she would again wander over to the window and press her face against the chilly glass. "I already had the baby," she thought, watching a piece of trapped twine being battered by the wind. "It's over. Things went wrong. I can't keep him." But her eyes searched and waited, and her arms sometimes formed a cradle with which to rock him.

And sometimes her arms stiffened with fear. Was she crazy, wanting to keep him? What kind of life would it be with a child who could never care for himself, who could smash like Humpty

Dumpty if she turned her back for an instant? What match was she, Julie Walters, for a staggering orthopedic handicap? She was no nurse, therapist, teacher. She wasn't even sure how she'd be as a mother. How did she dare to allow herself to dream of him?

She was hiding behind a garrison of noble sentiment, a mother longing for her baby; she knew herself that it was not so pure, so elementary. Never had she been much of an individualist; she was usually content to follow the prescribed patterns and her support was often with the opinion of the majority.

How then, was she to contend with the social stigma which plagued the handicapped? How firmly would she fare when her neighbors sent their round, robust babies past her door to seek playmates in similar good health? What of the splendid, rousing family reunions where congratulations were constantly being distributed; how much younger you look, darling, how beautiful your children, how eminently successful your life?

Without moving from her window, Julie knew that she had already taken leave of the burgeoning world of convention, of poised and punctilious fixed behavior. But where had she moved? Who was her companion in the other world? Perhaps it was only Martin, her broken baby.

✳

Every day she went out once, to the little grocery store across the street. There she bought Harold's hamburger or his spaghetti, and for herself, some cranberry juice and fresh luncheon rolls. The bread man came at about nine o'clock and Julie would watch him putting the packages on the shelf so that she knew which were the fresh ones.

After a while, he got so that he'd recognized her standing there and would hand her what she wanted before he put any of the other bread in its place.

Sometimes he would smile at her and say, "Got some nice, fresh twists today, miss. Croissants, they call them. What do you say?"

Shyly, Julie would shake her head. "No, but thank you."

He'd say, "Stick with the old faithful, huh?" and hand her the package of luncheon rolls, eight puffy little mountains with gleaming peaks of mahogany. On the wrapper it said, "Still only thirty-nine cents" and "Serve hot for fullest enjoyment." Julie never did. Then she would take her packages across the street to her building.

There she waited to ride up with an elevator operator who

always said "OK, folks" when he opened the door, even to a person alone. When she got to her apartment, she would fix herself some lunch. It took between eighteen and twenty-five minutes, depending on whether or not she had to wait for the bread man.

Harold's mother liked to call her at a time which was about halfway through her lunch. When the telephone began to ring, Julie took a last sip of her vodka and cranberry juice before going to pick up the receiver.

"Julie, dear. Good afternoon. Tell me, dear, how are you today?"

"Fine, Mother Walters, just fine. You, too?"

"We're all right, darling. Thank God. Are you improving? Feeling a little better today? Yesterday you didn't sound so good. I think, if you'll excuse my opinion, if you made yourself some breakfast, every morning like a religious observance . . ."

"I do make breakfast, Mother Walters. Every day." She bit into a roll.

"How is Harold, Julie dear?" She told her that Harold was fine.

"Now tell me," said her mother-in-law, "what you've been doing."

"Doing? Well, just the usual things, I suppose. Cleaning, shopping, a little laundry."

"Julie, how much do you pay for Harold's shirts? I always meant to ask you."

"Twenty-eight cents, Mother Walters. Why? Do you pay less for Pop's or something?"

"I certainly do, dear. I pay twenty-six cents around the corner from me and what's more, each shirt comes back in a plastic bag."

"A plastic bag," Julie pondered. "Well."

"Julie, I don't like to say this, but you sound funny to me."

"Funny?"

"Yes. Not right. I don't know, I can't explain it."

"It's probably because I was just in the middle of having my lunch, Mother Walters. I'll bet that's it."

"Oh," she said with relief. "No wonder. Sorry to interrupt, dear. What are you having?"

"A tuna fish on toast," Julie said into the receiver. "With lettuce. Harold always takes lettuce on his sandwiches. That was how I got into the habit."

No one mentioned the baby. It was as if he were not now, and never had been.

✳

After she cleared away the dinner, she stood in her place at the window.

"My mother thinks you should see a psychiatrist," Harold said from the brown sofa. She began to laugh, a soft, hollow spiral. Harold seemed stunned at the sound.

"What's so funny?" he asked.

"Your mother wanting me to go to a shrink," she said, "that's what. I thought her generation didn't believe in them. You know, all psychiatrists are supposed to be *meshugga*." She laughed again. "My God, she must think I'm an emergency." The laughter stopped. ". . . You think so too. Huh, Harold?"

✳

At first she had mutely clung to him, a stunned, bewildered creature, wounded yet alive. She will adjust, Harold thought. With time, she will accept it. These things are harder on a woman than on a man.

That was wrong. It was but a myth, a popular version of the meaning of parenthood. Every day, Harold gave the fiction a new validity as he consciously lightened his step, wore only the brightest of his ties, sometimes even whistled a little tune.

"Gee, Harold," they said to him at the office, "sorry to hear about the baby. How is your wife taking it?"

They were frightened, Harold knew, by what had happened to him and to Julie. By little Martin Walters, a shattered infant, who lay alone in a superbly padded crib miles away in another county, the self-assured were made to flinch.

With averted eyes, the secure scrutinized Harold's countenance for evidence of adversity. Show us, pleaded the confident, that you can lick anything if you just decide to put it out of your mind.

Harold said "Good morning," to every elevator operator. And at lunch, he was the first one finished with the crossword puzzle.

But often the printed word, to which he lately applied himself with unmitigated diligence, became blurred and shifty, and the raw, astonishing pain of reality held him paralyzed. It struck at him repeatedly and without warning. Nothing he could do would make it go away.

Sometimes he wanted to quit, to leave the job in which he performed precisely on schedule and exactly according to company policy, to join Julie at her window. The very perception of Martin Walters, his only son, what a blatant denial it was of the scheme of the universe, the harmony of the species; how futile seemed the time clock. God's will, they kept telling him. God's will. What kind of God was it who, in His Infinite Wisdom, wills a baby bones that disintegrate if you breathe on them?

If only he could forget the kid, pretend he'd never been born. Or else, when he thought of him, imagine this great American boy, ruddy, hearty, strong-boned. A boy who would leap into the school bus, toss the ball around on a grassy field, maybe play the drums in the school band. He'd find him the best set of snares made.

But not for this kid. For Martin Walters, irrevocably deviant, he'd be buying the finest plaster for casts and the best workmanship available in orthopedic devices. These were the least of the expenses. For Martin Walters, Harold knew, he would need to make provision for the entire length of the child's life.

Yet Harold Walters could not forget his son, though wiser men than he had decreed that the baby was bizarre and hopeless, and he would have been better off dead. He loved his child, misbegotten though he was, he loved him. It was eccentric of Harold. Not natural. It was nowhere to be found in the rules of good adjustment to life.

He therefore kept it to himself and never dared whisper it to anyone. Not even to Julie. But he began to wonder if the magnitude of her trouble might not be of the same specific origin as his. Perhaps it was that simple. Perhaps Julie loved the baby, too.

There was no discussion of their grief these days. Their preoccupation with the fate of Martin Walters had become a separate, isolated ache. Each privately considered the fact of his unabating sorrow to be a weakness, an unfashionable, stubborn propensity against accepting the inevitable. It was a secret shame which they could not even reveal to each other; no, it was not getting better.

But Harold was getting up on time and eating his breakfast. He was catching the right train to work. The findings in his written reports were still consummately objective and his syntax flawless. You would bet that Harold was somehow going to find his way.

He worried about Julie, for with her it was different. At first she seemed to weep without end, to cry out in the day and at night, to put to him the eternally unanswerable question: why had this befallen their lives? How did their simple wish for a home and children differ from that of their neighbors, to whom it was granted?

Soon after, she had fallen into a deep silence, and though she cleaned their brown furniture, and scrubbed their brown walls, and cooked him brown pieces of meat every night for dinner, the Julie who was his wife was gone, and there remained but a tenuous reminder of her, who stood patiently waiting at the courtyard window.

✳

"Go to a psychiatrist, or to a rabbi, or to anybody you please, Julie," he said, answering her accusation. "I don't care who it is. Go to anyone who can make you want to get out of the house, to talk to someone again. Other than for more luncheon rolls and new bottles of vodka."

"You know?" He nodded.

"Well, so what?" she asked, turning sharply. "At least it helps. Tell me, Harold, what's a psychiatrist going to do for me? Advise me that I'm not handling my problem maturely? Convince me that this yearning I feel for my substandard baby is unprecedented? That sophisticated adults don't, mustn't, shouldn't?"

He felt a surge of hope. It was the way that she used to put words together before. Exaggerating his helplessness, he laughingly would accuse her of being able to reduce the opposition, him, to total exhaustion when she argued for what she believed. Now the conviction in her voice surprised him. Their lives had long been silent and devoid of contact except for the muted, distant necessities, "Are the eggs done enough?"

"You yearn for him? For Martin? You yearn? Julie, you're disappointed, you're lonely, you're deprived, those feelings are different. Did you ever think about the kind of a life we would have with this baby, you and I, as husband and wife?"

She looked at him with quiet eyes, her flash fire now extinguished. "Did you ever think about the kind of life it is now?" she asked.

For the first time, pouring her drink and taking her roll, she ate her private meal in front of him.

✳

"We think," said Julie's father to Harold, calling him at the office, "that it might do Julie some good if she came to Florida with us. Get her a little sun and a change of scene. Cheer her up a little.

You never know, Harold. It might do the trick with her. She was always a very happy kid when she was belting around in that ocean, getting herself all tanned out. What do you say, m'boy?"

Harold knew that Julie's father's plan wouldn't work, that it had been conceived to lift the spirits of the child that she once had been, but was no longer. Yet it was a concrete proposal designed to restore his wife to him, to them, to life again. And in this aspect, the idea was irresistible. He told Julie's father that he'd talk to her about it.

✳

The hotel was a miniature city in itself, the hub of which was a vast expanse of flagstone intended for sunning, and an astonishing pool which wound and turned, curved and scalloped, strongly suggesting to the paying guest that this exceptional model epitomized the perfect holiday. Vacationing crowds surveyed each other's pressed new beach attire approvingly; how attractive everything was this year, how much better the choice of accommodations than in the past, how ideal, how ingenious, how impeccable.

Bronzed and ageless, with smiles which could reflect none but rapturous thoughts, American plan double occupancy subscribers had their profiles sketched in charcoal, ordered special drinks which were served in hollowed-out coconut shells, and danced the merengue to a band of goombay drums from Nassau even though it was only twenty minutes to eleven in the morning.

Beyond, there was a beach, a real beach, with sand and shells, and driftwood and seaweed which insisted upon washing ashore, no matter how often the hotel sent regiments of cleanup crews to do the job. Hardly anybody went to the beach except for children with their nurses and an occasional stray dog which had successfully stumbled through the outer maze of tennis courts and verandas, down through the terraced botanical displays and the mid-morning crafts class, arriving exultant at the gleaming wet shore.

Julie sat alone on the beach, making a sieve of her fingers. She watched the tough, abrasive grains of untouched white sand as they rushed through the opening, joining with the swift torrent downward. The scope of the mighty sun was vast and indiscriminate; it found her, it enveloped her, it caused her skin to smart and her eyes to narrow against the dazzling brightness. She was a misfit.

It laughed at her, this euphoria of a humanity on vacation

devoutly desiring both pleasure and perfection; it mocked her. At the image of her defective baby, it would look away. And at the knowledge of her voluntary association with him, it would withdraw, stealing off on tippy-toe.

Surrounded, she was unallied, a breed apart. And though she would endlessly wander from one carnival to another, carousing with the merrymakers, still she would be alone. She suspected of the world she was choosing that there was no vacation. And of the world she was in, that there surely was none.

❋

"She can't just sit down there for the whole time," said Julie's mother, "all alone like that. It's no good for her, always brooding, moody. Put some lotion on." They wore fringed hats of straw.

"Give her a chance, Doris. Don't rush her. It's only the first day."

"Still," her mother said, "I don't like it. I wish I could think of something that would snap her out of it. Maybe she'd like something . . . something . . ."

"Like what? A hamburger?"

"Like that cranberry juice drink she ordered on the plane. There was something she liked, Fred, you couldn't miss it. A Cranbreaker, they called it. I think you should order one for Julie. It'll do her good. Over there, Fred. The boy will bring it down to her."

The room clerk winked as Julie carried the tall glass back to her room. There she made the cool red liquid last while she wrote to her parents on stationery engraved with the wildly flourishing thicket of the hotel's emblem, changed out of her bathing suit and carefully fitted it back into her suitcase. Then Julie put on the clothes she had worn for the flight, and asked the bellboy to get her a cab.

❋

Harold would, she knew, be waiting at the airport. Her telegram would have made him uncertain, hesitant. His patient eyes would search her face, evaluate her demeanor: What now, Julie?

She would repeat what she had said in the telegram, right there in the terminal as faceless people dashed about in pursuit of their separate lives. She came back to get Martin, their baby, to bring him home, to try.

"Are you sure, Julie? Are you sure?" he would ask.

Then suddenly his eyes would brighten; it would be a trick, a decoy.

"Look Julie," he would say, "I've got an idea. We've still got time to catch the early show over at Cinema I. Then, we come out, grab a sandwich, and if we feel like it, go right next door and see what they've got at Cinema II. How does that sound, Julie? Remember? You used to love doing that."

"It's different now, Harold. Our lives. They're different."

"Are you sure, Julie? Are you sure?"

She would shake her head and say to him, "No, Harold. I'm not sure. I don't know if I can do it. And I'm not sure that it will work."

There would be a pause, an interval marked by a cantata of departure times and flight information.

"But you've come back to try," he would then say, knowing. "Okay, my dearie, let's have your baggage check."

And they would get into their car and drive off in another direction.

THE HANDICAPPED SOCIETY
*By Kathleen Lukens
and Carol Panter*

THE HANDICAPPED SOCIETY

Ugliness, like beauty, is only skin deep, but men can make it deeper. Because we see ourselves in the mirror of other people's eyes, how we look often becomes what we are. To be looked upon as ugly and worthless makes us feel ugly and worthless. That is why, though Nature handicaps, people's view of handicap handicaps, too.

It will not concern us here that blindness, mental deficiency, or cardiopathology strike at the eyes, brain or valves of the handicapped child. What matters to us and the child is that the handicap afflicts his visions, his mind and his heart. The child who is a cripple in the eye of his beholder comes to view himself with a crippling eye. The dull boy who is an idiot in the judgment of his fellows comes to see himself as worse than dull. Handicap is not just a mental or physical condition. It is a psychological condition. And it is also a social and moral condition. Handicap can afflict the soul.

The four preceding narratives are about handicapped children and their families. What concerns us is that these families, whether they cope well or ill with their child's disability, become handicapped themselves. Part of their handicap is psychological: those who spawn, harbor, or look upon suffering, ache. But most of their handicap is social. It appears that our unique cultural view of disability can be more crippling than poliomyelitis, more restrictive than cerebral palsy, to the child and the family to which he's bound.

"Handicapped" describes many things, including a social identity. In the social sphere handicapped people share with certain racial and ethnic minorities, the poor and the culturally deprived, an inferior status. Like the Negro competing with the white, the handicapped person is less likely to be educated up to his potential, less likely to win certain rewards such as money and prestige, and less likely to secure a satisfying social and occupational role, than the nonhandicapped.

Sometimes the handicapping condition, itself, severely limits the individual's choice of roles: the work role is an example. A physically disabled young man can't be a telephone lineman. Sometimes, changing conditions in the society create work problems, even as the diminishing number of unskilled jobs in America has adversely affected the mentally retarded. But according to the people who work in vocational rehabilitation, the greatest limitations on the handicapped worker spring not from these causes, but from prejudice and discrimination. People don't hire the handicapped because they don't like having them around.

Prejudice and discrimination are not intrinsic to chronic illness, deafness or brain injury. They create suffering quite apart from the physical or mental wounds of the handicap. Indeed, there is considerable evidence that most of the pain that accrues to handicap is not the product of the handicap itself, but rather a result of how the handicap is looked upon by the community, the family and the person involved (Cruickshank, 1955). Medication can control epilepsy. It can sometimes end seizures forever. But it cannot eliminate the fear in some people's minds that every Jekyll who is epileptic is also a potential Mr. Hyde.

Handicapped children are born into average families. Some kinds of birth defects occur more frequently in the lower classes, among the constitutionally inferior, or among the poorly fed. Some diseases claim the indigent more than others. But chronic disabilities are largely democratic. According to the National Health Survey, 1959–61, 18 percent of our children under seventeen are afflicted with a chronic physical condition. Disabilities strike the rich along with the poor, the ill-bred and the well-bred, the first-born and the last. They shape the sons of weight lifters and the daughters of Ph.D.'s into "the foolish things of the world to confound the wise, the weak things of the world to confound the mighty."

From birth or from the discovery of the handicap, the afflicted child does not merely change the life of the family. He makes its life (Robinson and Robinson, 1965). Whether he is mongoloid or severely physically disabled, he is often the one child who is not expected to grow up. He is the Tiny Tim, who is mocked, praised, teased, humored, coddled, cursed, loved, rejected; but around him, the family life revolves. He is the focus of marital discord, the theme of self-recrimination, the object of fraternal jealousy and embarrassment, the cross of family responsibility, the scapegoat of the neighbors, the hound of the family's sense of failure.

To be born into a family in any culture is to be born into a set of moral values. Chances are, the family to which the hurt child belongs has stressed along with the contemporary culture: conformity, respectability, success, education and good health. The child's existence conflicts with these values and precipitates a crisis in the family (Robinson and Robinson, 1965). According to the parents of newly diagnosed mongoloid children, they wept, were hysterical, vomited, had diarrhea, were numb and often wished to die (Kramm, 1963). "I felt as if I were bleeding inwardly and desperately," author Pearl Buck wrote of her discovery that her daughter was severely retarded. ". . . Death would be far easier to bear, for death is final" (Buck, 1950).

On the surface, at least, it appears that the families of the handicapped are not repelled primarily by the physical suffering of the child or even by the permanence of his condition. "Normal" illnesses such as measles, a broken leg, or scarlet fever do not create such shock waves. What perturbs these parents, it appears, is the stigma of abnormality that accrues to the handicapped in our culture, a stigma which the parents not only share with their child but one they think they deserve. Having accepted and adhered to the typically American cultural values without evaluation or review, they are suddenly confronted with a child whose very presence contradicts them. Success is what is valued, and the child has no potential for success. Likewise, the parents have offended their own system of values, for they did not succeed in bearing a normal child. Relatives and friends gather to exude pity for the couple and dismay at the prospect of their child, their lips echoing one of the most popular moral judgments of our age, "poor so-and-so, he's surely better off dead." It becomes clear to the new parents, if it was not clear at once, that they have brought abnormality into a world with an abnormal desire to be normal.

According to social psychologist Roger Brown, the social devaluation of one's child results in self-devaluation. Having spawned a child whose very existence is not socially sanctioned, the parents are immediately divested of the expectations of prestige, status, and pride in their child's future accomplishments that usually accrue to the middle class. No Shakespeare, no Leonardo ornaments their fantasy; no dreams may be dreamed for such a child. The parents experience themselves as isolated, devaluated and socially estranged. The future, which to other men bears hope, brings a lifetime of extra costs to them, those medical and educational tolls that social indifference forces them to bear.

To achieve family harmony, the handicapped parents must either alter their own value system to escape the cultural values of success and normalcy; alter the value system of society; or somehow change the condition of the child. The questions and doubts that plague handicapped families in our culture are real but not necessarily relevant. For example, such questions as "What good is the child? (or his parents as his progenitors), or "Is his life worthwhile?" imply that children ought be profitable investments with quantitative value to their parents. As long as the handicapped family continues to cling to a value system that implies life ought to show a profit (Fromm, 1955), it is not surprising that, according to the experts, family harmony is rarely achieved.

Accepted values, easily confused with eternal verities, are hard to change even when they are shown to be without rational or visceral basis, and even when they do much harm. Reactions of fear and disgust to the disabled are assumed to be natural when they may in fact be only prevalent. There is some evidence that apes recoil from fellow apes who assume the abnormal postures of the disabled (Hebb and Thompson, 1954). On the other hand, there are human societies which honor epileptics, blind men or schizophrenics, attributing to them that mystical sensitivity reserved in our culture to abstruse poets and Italian film directors.

The notion that the handicapped are less deserving appears to be the heir of the old Puritan economic ethic. In an age of scarcity and at a time when men were cutting a world out of the wilderness, it was necessary that all men work. Because the handicapped could not work, their lack of productivity was undoubtedly viewed as damaging to society. Today, when productivity is so high the government has to pay farmers not to produce, we continue to cling to the criterion of productivity as the measure of a man, and a yardstick of his value to society. "What good is he?" or "What's she worth?" may be without social or moral relevance in an age of affluence but they are questions that continue to be asked. By the same token, men and women in our society continue to view themselves in terms of some socially useful function they perform. If one were to ask the man on the street who he is, his answer would be something like this: "I'm a dentist"; "I'm a student"; "I'm a housewife with two children." "Identification of function," writes the author of *The Tower and the Abyss*, "is the admittance ticket granting the right to exist." The handicapped man whose intrinsic value is as unmeasurable as any other man's, may serve no socially useful function. He has no ticket. He is loathe to answer, "I'm a cripple."

There are profound psychological reasons why some men need to castigate the leper and other men seek a scapegoat of a different religion or race. It is not within our scope to explore those reasons here. But it is not the duty of society to provide institutions and uphold conventions that justify the perversity of men. The goal of society is justice.

The dearth of social institutions for the handicapped expresses callously the frailty of our committment to the frail. Like a Kikuyu tribesman searching for a familiar face on the streets of Peoria, Illinois, the paraplegic looks in vain for the elevator in the county courthouse, the blind man for the braille books in the library. A path for the handicapped from nursery school through college to marriage and work is, in most communities, either not there or else not socially sanctioned. According to a recent study, forty percent of orthopedically handicapped young adults listed church attendance as the only social activity in which they took some part (Brieland, 1967; Carlsen, 1957). Unless the child is in a custodial institution, who does he play with, where and how does he discover his group identity, who are "his own kind" of people? When he grows up, "Would you want your daughter to marry one?" Even the dubious joys of belonging to and participating in the values of a persecuted minority are denied to the handicapped child.

Society does not permit the ordinary parent to control so important a matter as the education of his normal child. But in the case of the disabled or retarded, not a single state compels their attendance at a school and few states offer adequate instruction to the child who comes on his own. Yet in a society based upon achieved rather than ascribed status, education and eventually work, determine the specific social class to which an individual belongs. To deny the mildly handicapped adequate instruction is to deprive them of the symbols of success. To deny the moderately handicapped adequate instruction is to deprive them of the means to an independent life. To deny the severely handicapped, particularly the mentally and sensorily impaired, adequate instruction is to deprive them of the consciousness of life.

Despite how deep their stakes in education, the handicapped are, nonetheless, denied. Why are they denied? Why are Negroes denied? According to the man on the street: "because there isn't enough money for schools for normal kids"; "because there aren't enough jobs around for whites." Every dollar that goes to a disabled child, it is assumed, is taken from a normal child, just as every job that goes to a Negro, it is assumed, is taken from a white. Thus, it is not only implied that cripples and Negroes constitute a threat to the normal and the white, but that the crippled child and the Negro man are inherently less deserving of the fruits of what we call a decent life.

America's attitude toward social injustice, including handicap, is like St. Augustine's when he prayed, "Lord make me chaste, but not now." Americans want to eliminate all social injustices, in time and with money. What is required, it appears, is not so much time or money but a change of heart.

The reader may protest, for example, that it is not social bias that limits the number of social institutions created for the handicapped but the faith that disability is disappearing. "Look what happened to polio and T.B.!" Handicap will recede before the march of scientific progress even as poverty ebbs before increasing output. However theoretically sound these observations seem, the fact is that handicaps do not lessen but increase. Statistics on the increasing rate of congenital anomalies, along with the decreasing number of doctors and public health nurses, and the absolute loss in the quantity of prenatal care are impressive (Fishbein, 1963). Suffice it to say, by 1975 there will be 75 million children in America and there'll be nine million with chronic handicaps: enough to populate New Jersey (Cooke, 1964). Today, there is a handicapped child in one out of every nine families.

Then, what about costs? The expense of special education is at least twice as great as regular instruction while vocational rehabilitation raises the bill. The paucity of social institutions for the handicapped might more eloquently express philosophic individualism than some darker side of man's social nature. It may be so, but if so, individualism is an irrelevant extravagance, it being demonstrably cheaper to face up to social problems than neglect them. The costs of Negro poverty and Negro crime not only to the wasted individual but to the taxpayer's pocketbook are paralleled by the expense of institutionalization and public support of the handicapped. For example, the American public paid out $300 million to custodial institutions that cared for only 4 percent of the mentally retarded in 1962 alone (Stevens and Heber, 1964). Mentally retarded people who don't work get some $124 million every year in disability and welfare payments. What they would be worth if they worked is $5 billion every year (National Association for Retarded Children, *Facts*).

The profits from investment in human beings tend to be immodestly higher than the profits from investment in, say, blast furnaces. The New Jersey Rehabilitation Commission reported that it had rehabilitated 4,000 mentally and physically handicapped people in 1965. It cost the state less than $900 apiece to unleash their productive capacity and enhance their social value. But, more significant for the purpose of our discussion, within a year, these handicapped people had earned over eleven million dollars of which $1.4 million was paid by them in taxes.

Finally, the reader may argue, that thanks to the declining importance of production, the Social Darwinian dread of making tolerable the lives of the unfit or unproductive is surrendering to the new compassion of affluence. Our society, it is claimed, grows progressively more philanthropic. And, surely, it cannot be denied. More than four million children were enrolled in some kind of costly special education, public and private, in 1960. The Elementary and Secondary Education Act was amended in 1967 to include federal assistance to special schools, remedial services and other aids to handicapped children. New Jersey passed a model law in 1966 making mandatory the education of the emotionally disturbed and neurologically impaired. Sheltered workshops and vocational training programs spring up in the more progressive states. Thanks to the powerful moral influence of the Kennedy family, Congress allots more millions every year to research in mental deficiency, adding to the sums spent to combat most diseases that cripple and destroy. It is as gauche to wince before a cripple as to tell a Negro to sit in the back of the bus.

But just as the Negro rails against the rhetorical philanthropy and anemic efforts of the white liberal, so the handicapped might wisely mistrust the good will that passes for performance. Kind words and half measures obscure the villains of stalemate and inertia. They deny the fact that there is a conflict between the stigmatized individual and the society that perpetrates his stigma. This denial is bad for our civilization. It is worse for the handicapped child and the handicapped family.

It is bad to begin with because it hides the truth that however dramatic the educational progress of the past few years, the drama of failure is equally compelling. For the four million children in special classes in 1960, for example, there were only 25,000 special teachers; that's one to every 1,600 pupils. Of the half-million motor handicapped children in the country in 1960, less than 4 percent were enrolled in public school classes, even though education is supposedly every child's right. The vast majority of this nation's blind children had to be sent away for segregated learning in all blind private schools where they were allegedly taught to live in a world that can see. Only one state saw fit to set up special instruction for aphasic children, who can hardly speak if they speak at all. Only a few states taught the brain-injured; fewer still, the emotionally disturbed. Philanthropic or not, this is still not the Age of the Lame, the Halt and the Blind.

The failure of our civilization to keep pace with the needs of its burgeoning handicapped population, the failure, in short, of our society to gear itself to the abnormal as well as the normal, is a moral failure and must be recognized as such. Just as the admission of the leaders of government to the Negro that "we have been wrong about you" has raised Negro morale, permitted aggressive feeling to flow outward instead of inward, and reduced self-hatred and drug addiction in the ghetto, so the lack of such an admission to the handicapped continues to imprison the disabled and their families in the values that insure guilt and defeat.

Anxious to regain an improved self-picture but burdened with a child estranged from the goals and experience of their friends, many families struggle to exhibit normalcy and to eschew the signs of difference and of conflict. The child's defects and disabilities are to be concealed at any cost, even at the price of functioning. Didn't the doctor say, "Have him lead as normal a life as possible"? Thus, parents whose children have learning disabilities frequently demand that their child be allowed to "pass" for normal in a regular

class even though a segregated, special class might be better geared
to respond to his disability. A diabetic or epileptic school child is
made to risk acidosis or an epileptic "fit" unnecessarily because his
parents dare not tell the school he's different. So great are the
pressures toward normalcy and so great the stigma attached to
abnormalcy as parents perceive it, that the appearance of health is
frequently exchanged for health itself. According to rehabilitation
psychologists Neff and Weiss (in Wolman, 1965), many parents
prefer a passive, realistic-looking limb for their amputee children or
no prosthesis at all over the functional but noncosmetic hook.
They report that particularly in America, parents of these children
overwhelmingly resist certain cineplastic operations that come
closest to restoring function because they are so unpleasant in
appearance.

There is much evidence that parents who struggle to conceal
their children's handicaps are not necessarily unrealistic. When the
public decrees that a handicapped child ought to compensate for
his handicap, it does not have in mind the child dragging his legless
body across the floor. What it has in mind is a child, sitting,
looking normal, his leglessness concealed beneath a blanket, his
handicap offering no offense. Considering the evidence that children with nonvisible defects make better life adjustments than
children with visible disabilities (Cruickshank, 1955), is it fair to
castigate parents who seek to normalize their children?

Actually, there is considerable emphasis in the literature on the
failure of handicapped families to adjust to the demands of their
situation, but little stress on the inevitability of conflict when even
well-adapted, normally status-minded people give birth to a social
misfortune. While there is professional concern with the child,
there is little concern, says psychologist S. B. Sarason, for those
individuals who love the child but whose life goals have suddenly
been shattered. There is interest in teaching maladjusted individuals
how to adapt to society as it is, but no interest in changing a society
that makes individuals what they are. Yet the question continues to
arise whether the problems of the handicapped family stem primarily from individual neuroses, or rather from objectively real
social pressures; from parental mismanagement of the child, or
from a social bias that limits the child at every level.

Since social institutions have failed to create a permanent, digni-
fied place in their midst for the handicapped as they have for the

normal, there is no one to plan the life of the child. While professionals have concerned themselves with the negative aspects of parental handling, they are themselves not able to offer advice, give specific directions, or encourage the kind of planning parents so desperately need (Sarason, 1959). Rarely can they answer such questions as: "Where shall I send my child to school?"; "Will they take epileptics at a summer camp?"; "Shall I tell the nursery school my child's retarded?"

Without the traditional or institutional guidelines, without the emotional and intellectual confidence of families dealing with the familiar, the parents, by default, set the course the child will take. Some parents of the blind, for example, will decide that their child will live in the world of the sighted even though he can't compete there on equal terms. Others will determine that their child will live in the world of the blind where he can, at least, find acceptance and security. Whichever course they opt for, their child's life is unlikely to be fulfilled. The professionals may discover neurotic denial in the first choice and neurotic overprotection in the second, and yet it is difficult to see how parents without social, institutional or professional guidance can avoid such extremes, man being neither all good, all loving, nor all wise.

The rearing of a handicapped child requires the forging of a new set of values by the family that can effectively compete with the moral system of society. The parents must convey to their blind child, for example, that the loss of an important tool does not make him a "bad" or "unfit" person, that the loss need not rule out a valuable life if he can only see value in himself. Parents have to change their system of worth and unworth so they are free to recognize that a conflict exists between their child's best interests and what everybody thinks. Too often like the newly afflicted Job, parents accept their suffering as their due ("The Lord giveth and the Lord taketh away; Blessed be the Name of the Lord"), not uttering a word of protest to society. But even as Job came to see he was innocent, once the parents have absolved themselves of guilt, they can turn their self-recrimination outward, and as Job demanded a reason or remission for his suffering, the parents ask the same of society.

One indication that such a change is possible has been the organization of parent pressure groups across the country whose aim is to press for improvements in public policy towards the handicapped. Although these groups include organizations that have been in existence for a generation or more, like the United Cerebral Palsy Association, most of them, such as the Association for Brain-Injured Children and the National Association for Retarded Children, reflect the development of a group identity on the part of handicapped families and probably represent the turning of guilt and self-hatred once directed against themselves as bearers of handicapped children, towards the society which exacerbates the handicap. While the older groups like the cerebral palsy and polio foundations have been made up largely of professional and laymen without handicapped children, the new groups follow the pattern of the newer civil rights groups in that they have less money, more energy per capita, and are composed of and officered by those directly affected by social bias, i.e. the parents of the handicapped.

While these groups have pressed for and obtained special instruction and recreation for their special children in many places, even exerting political influence in the New York gubernatorial race of 1966, it cannot be said that most of these groups have yet recognized the need to create an alternative sociomoral climate for the handicapped. Too often, in fact, dedicated as they are to improved conditions for only those children with a specific defect, they fail to see their common cause with other organizations differently committed but with the same social handicap. Thus, it is not uncommon for parents of cerebral palsied children to work for legislation that consciously discriminates against children with other forms of brain damage; for the parents of mentally retarded children to refuse to let their child play with what they see as the less valued emotionally disturbed, and vice versa; or for all or any to adopt competitive and thwarting attitudes toward the culturally deprived.

In general, these groups reflect the prevailing middle-class mode in every way but one: children with their disability have been denied. And yet in their press for certain changes in the school and society, they find it feasible at times to work together with parents of children with other handicaps, find it expedient to use the rhetoric of fraternalism and come to believe in what they say. The shortcomings of such groups ought not obscure their importance and their value. Through associations with parents of like mind and like suffering, parents of handicapped children come to focalize less on their child's affliction and more on what they can do about it in a collective and constructive way, with advantages to themselves, their child, and society.

No critique of our society should end without acknowledging the presence in that society of those exceptionally normal people who have the freedom and power to value those who need most to be valued. Wherever there is a project for the deaf, a camp for the crippled, a Scout troop for the dumb, there are those who love in the midst of them. It is not only the ones who teach, who counsel or who heal that serve, but all those who feel the wounds of other men and who see there is a man beyond his wounds. It is these people, and this capacity in all people, that offers the greatest hope for the handicapped in any age. Having made humanity and having nurtured it, the love of man for man may yet, in our time, set man free.

✳

The purpose of this essay has been to provide a perspective through which the four preceding narratives might be viewed. Hopefully, the reader will have discovered in the stories that the handicapped families who recognized the intrinsic human value of their child fared better than those who saw him as a social abstraction and, thus, as a social misfortune. In summary, the problems of the handicapped child are not the simple facts of physical or mental disadvantage. For it is not so much the handicap itself that cheats the handicapped of life. It is more the way the disabled view themselves and how their disabilities are viewed by others. Thus, the problems of the handicapped child are the problems of the handicapped family. For it is the family that first looks upon the child, and it is through them that the child discovers how he looks. The problems of the family with a handicapped child are not just the problems of handicap. For it is not just the drab, lonely caring for the child that makes theirs a handicapped family. It is rather their fear, their anxious, guilt-provoking dread of the rejecting, damning power of society; a society which may itself be handicapped.

Society is composed of men, and men can have the faith that each child is born with the power to be human. For most, the power readily unfolds, growing naturally; the brain need only hold to its promises, the body keep its biologic faith. For others, those to whom the wholeness of body and mind have been denied, humanness lies in wait—for science, for good will, for parental concern, true. But it also waits for other men's involvement: for their valuing what they had not thought to value; for their changing what they did not want to change; for their loving whom they had not thought to love.

Bibliography for "The Handicapped Society"

1. Brieland, Donald. "A Followup Study of Orthopedically Handicapped High School Graduates," *Exceptional Children*, April, 1967, pp. 555–565.
2. Buck, Pearl. *The Child Who Never Grew*. New York, N.Y.: John Day Co., 1950.
3. Carlsen, Anne H. "Vocational and Social Adjustment of Physically Handicapped Students," *Exceptional Children*, March, 1957, pp. 364–368.
4. Cooke, Robert, E. "Freedom from Handicap," *The Special Child in Century 21*. Edited by J. Hellmuth. Seattle, Wash.: Special Child Publications, 1964.
5. Cruickshank, William M. "Psychological Considerations with Crippled Children," *Psychology of Exceptional Children and Youth*. Edited by William M. Cruickshank. Englewood Cliffs, N.J.: Prentice-Hall, Inc., 1955.
6. *Encyclopedia of Educational Research*, 3rd edition. Edited by Chester Harris. New York, N.Y.: The Macmillan Company, 1960.
7. *Facts on Mental Retardation*. National Association for Retarded Children, 420 Lexington Ave., New York, N.Y.
8. Fishbein, Morris. *Birth Defects*. Philadelphia, Pa.: J. B. Lippincott, 1963.
9. Fromm, Erich. *The Sane Society*. Holt, Rhinehart and Winston, New York, N.Y., 1955.
10. Kahler, Eric, *The Tower and the Abyss*. New York, N.Y.: George Braziller, 1958.
11. Kramm, Elizabeth R. *Families of Mongoloid Children*. Washington Dept. of Health, Education and Welfare, Children's Bureau, 1963.
12. Neff, W. S., and Weiss, S. A. "Psychological Aspects of Disability," *Handbook of Clinical Psychology*. Edited by B. B. Wolman, New York, N.Y.: McGraw-Hill, 1965.
13. Newman, Joseph. "Psychological Problems of Children and Youth with Chronic Medical Disorders," *Psychology of Exceptional Children and Youth*. Edited by William M.